CLASSIC
HASSIDIC
TALES

CLASSIC HASSIDIC TALES

MARVELLOUS TALES OF RABBI ISRAEL
BAAL SHEM AND OF HIS GREAT-GRAND-
SON, RABBI NACHMAN, RETOLD FROM
HEBREW, YIDDISH AND GERMAN SOURCES

BY

MEYER LEVIN

ILLUSTRATED BY
MAREK SZWARC

DORSET PRESS
NEW YORK

This edition published by Dorset Press, a division of Marboro Books
Corporation, by arrangement with the Estate of Meyer Levin
and Scott Meredith Literary Agency Inc.
1985 Dorset Press

ISBN 0-88029-037-4

Printed in the United States of America

1 2 3 4 5 6 7 8 9 10

CONTENTS

ILLUSTRATIONS

FOREWORD

TWO hundred years ago, in a remote hut in the Carpathian Mountains, there lived a wonder-worker named Rabbi Israel. Some now say that he never existed; the like has been said of King Arthur and of Jesus Christ; their legends remain with us. Some say that Israel was never a rabbi, but rather an unlearned peasant who took authority unto himself. It is told that even as a child he deserted the village schoolroom to run into the woods where he learned the speech of animals and birds, of trees, stones, and flowers.

A grown man, he knew all the secret mysteries of Cabbala; but he refused to lead the stifled life of the synagogue scholar, turned his back upon the rabbinical bickerings and pin-point disputes over minutae of the law, and withdrew to the mountains, where he earned his livelihood as a lime-burner, and where he would wander alone, sometimes for many days, absorbed in his strange reflections.

When Israel came down from the mountains to Medzibuz it was to teach men to live with abounding joy, for joy in every living thing, he said, is the highest form of worship. The woods were holy, and the fields, every stone and blade of grass contained a spark of the living Soul; every act of living: breathing, eating, walking should be accomplished with fervour, joy, ecstasy, for every act spoke to God.

Scholars who had passed their pale youth huddled over tomes of the law lifted their heads and for the first time saw the sky; he drew them out of the murky synagogue into the open fields; there, too, he said, God would hear them.

He did not violate tradition; he enlarged it. He was observant of every point of the law, and he revered the house of prayer; but he said again that divinely simple truth that becomes lost in the ritual of every religion; he said that the full-hearted desire to worship was more important than the form or place of worship.

Disciples gathered about him; soon legends began to grow of the wondrous deeds and teachings of Rabbi Israel, and then he was called the Baal Shem Tov, which means the Master of the Wondrous Name. By that Name, he had the power to do miraculous deeds. He went from one end of the earth to the other in the space of a single night; he conquered the wild boars that the sorcerers set upon him; he pierced the iron wings that shrouded the earth from heaven; he drew the dead bride from her untimely grave.

For a thousand years the Jewish folk genius for the creation of myth had made no new body of legend. But now the genius that had made the unsurpassable tales of the bible and the gem-like parables of the Talmud was turned back to its natural sources, and at once it began to weave the marvellous fabric of the legend of the Baal Shem Tov.

He had stood in the market-place, telling his fables to the entranced people who gathered about him while the rabbi of the town preached to an empty synagogue. In their huts of a Sabbath, his followers repeated the strange meaningful fables he had uttered, and told tales of the miraculous deeds he had done. Pilgrims came to Medzibuz, and carried home with them the tales of the Baal Shem Tov. Soon his followers numbered in the hundreds, and they became known as the Chassidim. The word Chassid implies intense piety, ardour, fervour, ecstasy.

Despite the opposition of many noted rabbis, who accused him of ignorance, of wizardry, of Sabbath-violation, the number of Israel's followers grew, for his teaching had that beauteous simplicity that goes directly to the hearts of the common folk. The secrets and delights of heaven were no longer reserved for the scholars who could pass all their days and nights in the house of study; the water-carrier and the mule-driver could gather around the long table in the hut of the Master, and take part in the discussion.

After several generations, the Chassidim numbered half the Jewry of Eastern Europe. They were governed by their Tsadikim, or exalted saints, to whom they came for decision on every conceivable occasion. If a merchant of Brody could not make up his mind whether or not to go to Lemberg to buy goods, he asked his Tsadik; if a housewife did not know whether or not an egg was pure, she asked her Tsadik; if a father did not know whether or not a certain match was suitable for his daughter, he asked his Tsadik. The power of the Tsadik was transmitted in his family, so that soon veritable dynasties of Chassidic rabbis were established.

Soon, too, the decline of the movement set in, for many of the latter Tsadikim took advantage of their power, lived in pomp and luxury, and even sold the honour of being seated next to them at table. The meaning of Chassidism was lost; pleasure took the place of joy, and orgy of ecstasy.

There are still hundreds of thousands of Chassidim, many of them true to the original meaning of their belief; and among them, true Tsadikim are to be found.

But the last to attain the exaltation of the Baal Shem Tov was his own great-grandson, Rabbi Nachman of Bratzlaw. In him, the Chassidic legend had its fulfilment and its completion.

Folk literature has two sources. The tales may grow imperceptibly as they pass among the people, each teller adding his words, until the image is complete; or they may be made in entirety by one who is so completely within his folk as to speak with the voice of the entire people. The Chassidic legend is drawn from both these sources.

The legends of the Baal Shem Tov have no single authorship; they were made partly from the Baal Shem's sayings, partly by story-tellers who went from town to town repeating the tales; one of the legends is concerned with what happened to such a story-teller. Later, the tales were written down, and to this day they are circulated by the hundreds of thousands in little penny-story-books printed in every city of Poland and Russia. Many generations of Jewish children had no other Arabian Nights than these Chassidic tales, whose glamorous adventures they absorbed while their parents discussed the deep meanings concealed in the same fables. At last scholars, philosophers, and literary men discovered the legends, and such masters as Israel Zangwill, Sholom Asch, S. Ansky, and the German poet-philosopher Martin Buber have made use of them.

But the second part of the Chassidic legend is composed of the tales of a single author: Rabbi Nachman. Here the individual speaks as the folk, and we have

a group of seeming fairy tales that are lucid and
meaningful as the parables of Christ. Over the table
on Sabbath eve, or during long wagon-journeys in the
Galician provinces, on walks, or when teaching his
students, Rabbi Nachman would spin these marvellous illusions, in which Kings and Princes, Heroes and
Demons move in colourful transparency, like majestic
figures of a stained-glass window set into speech and
motion. Each tale is an intricate maze; the reader
follows seven different paths, only to find himself suddenly standing, bewildered and triumphant, at their
common cross-roads. The meaning is hidden and yet
shining clear, for each person in each tale is a symbol
as abstract as a numeral, and at the end, the symbols
seem miraculously to have taken their places in the
pure formula of a given theorem. There is the story
of the King (God) who unwittingly sends his beloved
Daughter (the Shechina, Glory of God) into the place
of the Evil One (Earth); then He grieves at her loss
until the Prince (Israel of the Messiah) goes out to
find her. Twice he meets her but fails, through his
own weakness, in delivering her from the palace of
the Evil One; twice he must wait in the desert (Egypt
and Babylon); the third time he is sent wandering
over the earth (the present exile); but at last he comes
to her in the Palace of Pearls upon the Golden Mountain (the Holy Land); he remains there a long time,
and then they return to the King (but how the return
is effected, we do not know).

This might be the place for an essay on Chassidic
doctrine; I am no scholar, but merely another story-
teller who, from a far land and through a strange
tongue, has come upon a saga of his own people, and

recognized it, and felt that he must tell it again. Chassidic doctrines have been explained, beautifully so by Martin Buber, whose essays on Chassidism, together with his versions of some of these same tales, have recently been published in an English translation by Lucy Cohen.

And yet it has seemed to me that an outline of doctrine would be superfluous as an introduction to these tales, for the tales themselves were used by the Chassidic rabbis to explain that very doctrine. Rabbi Nachman's fable of the Princess lost in the palace of the Evil One is an example of their magnificent clarity and beauty.

For we may explain the Chassidic conception of the Soul as embracing all things and beings on earth: for God sent his Living Glory, called the Shechina, down to earth, and the sparks of Living Glory are in all things: the rocks, the trees, the grass of the field, the caterpillar, the eagle, and the lion, and in man. The soul of each thing and of each man is part of the Universal Soul, and at the awaited time, when Messiah comes, the sparks will flow together, and return to unite with God. The flaw is in man, and the Evil One prevents his arriving at the time of perfection that will bring down Messiah. But is not all this told in Rabbi Nachman's tale?

The Evil One himself is part of Universal Glory, for he has known suffering. Then all that happens on earth, even evil, should be met with joy in the universality of the Soul, for the descent is part of the rise, and sin is necessary to purity. But this, too, is beautifully made clear in the tale of Rabbi Israel who as a boy held the twitching black heart of the Enemy in his hand, and would not destroy it, because he saw that it, too, suffered. And again, in Rabbi Nachman's tale of the Prince Who Was Made Entirely of Precious Stones, but had to become a leper before his gem-like beauty was revealed.

We may explain the Chassidic belief in the union of souls predestined for each other, but that is beautifully and dramatically told by Rabbi Israel in " Two Souls "; we may tell of the Chassidic conception of the voice of the soul, or the Melody in each Thing, but Rabbi Nachman's story of the " King's Son and the Servant's Son " almost makes us hear that very melody; we may repeat the Chassidic principle that the form of worship is insignificant beside the emotion, but no abstract words can ever make that as clear as the tale of the shepherd who worshipped God by leaping back and forth over a brook!

These are the imaginings of obscure rabbis who lived long ago in remote villages along the River Dneister and the River Bog, and yet the work of our modern men of intellect and sophistication does not go beyond their fundamental conceptions, for no one can go beyond truth. The modern conception of Time as non-existent, elaborated in Professor Einstein's formulae, is exquisitely stated in Rabbi Nachman's " Tale of the Seven Beggars "; and so sophisticated an author as Professor Erskine bases his latest novel upon the fable of the man who was sent back from the gates of heaven to complete whatever good deeds or bad he had left unfinished on earth, for order is the universal key; and that, too, is part of Chassidic doctrine, and is told in the story of the Baal Shem and the little horse.

To my knowledge, this is the first attempt to tell the Chassidic legend in English. I have read the tales in many collections in Yiddish, Hebrew, and German; and I have tried to be merely another story-teller, receiving the legends from his forebearers, choosing of the many tellings of the same tales those that please him most, adding his own little turns and touches to the fables, and telling them again, but trying always to keep in them the spirit of the tale told in a warm hut to many eager hearers.

In the more mystical portions of some of the stories of Rabbi Israel, the interpolations of Martin Buber have seemed so just as to become an integral part of the myth, and I have therefore followed closely his versions of " Israel and the Enemy," " The Book of Mysteries," " The Wandering in Heaven," and " The Prophecy of the New Year," and have used his story in combination with tales from other sources in the account of the Baal Shem's attempted voyage to Palestine.

I have tried to put the scattered legends of the Baal Shem Tov together so as to form a legendary life-story of Rabbi Israel, who was born in 1700 in Okup and died in 1760 in Medzibuz. His great-grandson, who was born in Medzibuz in 1772, and died in Uman in 1810, left thirteen tales, which were written down by his pupil, Nathan. Of these, I have here translated eleven; the other two are fragmentary and confused.

Many of these tales I first heard from the lips of Marek Szwarc, of Lodz and Paris, a true Chassid and a great artist. To him I am profoundly grateful. I wish also to thank the Jewish novelist, Sholom Asch, for the loan of his excellent collection of Chassidic literature; and to express my indebtedness to Leo Schwarz, of New York, for his scholarly aid, especially in relation to the Rabbi Nachman sources.

MEYER LEVIN

New York, 1932

THE BAAL SHEM TOV
Rabbi Israel, Master of the Holy Name

BEFORE HE WAS BORN

HERE IS THE STORY OF HOW ELIJAH CAME TO GOD,
AND ASKED HIM TO MAKE RABBI ELEAZER THE
FATHER OF RABBI ISRAEL; AND OF
THE MARVELLOUS TRIALS OF
RABBI ELEAZER

WHEN God was about to create Adam, a number of souls, knowing that all of the souls then living in heaven would share in the sin of created Adam, fled to a far place outside the boundaries of heaven, and hid themselves in a corner of chaos. There they waited until after the first sin was done.

Only that band of hidden souls escaped the evil touch of Adam's sin. And they are the Innocent souls.

When the Enemy becomes powerful on earth, and stretches mountains of black clouds between man's earth and heaven, when men become knotted with evil and lose their Godly form, then the Almighty goes up to the highest of his regions, and seeks out one of his Innocent souls.

He says to the Innocent soul, " Go down and purify the earth."

Such were the souls of Abraham, of Isaac, and of Jacob; such was the soul of Noah; such were the souls of the great prophets, of the great scribes, and of the great rabbis. The soul of the Messiah is prince among this band of Innocent souls; and when the time of Redemption arrives, Messiah himself will come down from the highest of heavens. Then the Enemy will disappear forever.

The soul of Rabbi Israel, the Baal Shem Tov, was one of that band of innocents who escaped the sin of Eden. And this is how he came to be born on earth.

In a hamlet in the district of Moldau there lived the pious Rabbi Eleazer. His wife was a virtuous woman; she was the daughter of a pious Jew of the city of Okup.

Tartars attacked the valleys of Moldau, pillaged the villages, slaughtered many Jews, and carried off others into slavery. Rabbi Eleazer was one of those taken captive.

His wife said, " I will wait for his return until the end of my days, and if he does not return to me in this world, I will meet him in the next world."

In heaven, Elijah came to God and said, " See how the Jews suffer. It is time to send an Innocent soul down to earth, to sweeten the lives of the Jews."

God said, " Not yet."

For many weeks Eleazer voyaged with the barbarians. On land, he was forced to carry heavy burdens. On sea, he was chained to an oar and made to row as a galley slave.

At last, coming to a strange shore, the Tartars took the Jew into the city and sold him in the market-place as a slave.

He was purchased by the King's Grand Vizier, who soon perceived that the slave, though of a race unknown to him, was a person of unusual intelligence.

Rabbi Eleazer had kept count of the days. When Sabbath came, he begged his master to permit him to rest on that day. This the Vizier granted, and Rabbi Eleazer did not work on Sabbath.

The only duty of Rabbi Eleazer, when he was a slave, was to watch for the time when his master the Vizier returned from his audience with the King; then Rabbi Eleazer would wash the feet of the Grand Vizier.

Thus, the slave had a great deal of time to pass. Rabbi Eleazer knew by heart the Psalms of David, and he passed his days singing the Psalms.

He was not happy, for he felt himself alone away from his people, and he prayed God that he might be released to go home to his wife and to live among other Jews.

At last he could bear his life in the court no longer, and he thought of flight. One night he crept from his bed and made his way through the halls of the palace, until he reached the gate. There he saw the guard asleep. His naked sword, fallen from his hand, lay at his side. The keys were bound to his girdle.

Rabbi Eleazer looked at the sword and said to himself, " To take the keys I must lift the sword and slay the man."

Instead, he returned and remained in captivity.

One year, the King besieged a neighbouring city. The city was strong and withstood his attack. Then the King did not know what to do; he asked of his advisers whether his army should continue to stand in their boats on the river before the walls of the city, becoming themselves weaker while they waited for the enemy to weaken, or whether he should risk all of his men in a charge upon the walls.

The Vizier did not know what advice to give, and fell therefore into disfavour with the King. When the Vizier came home, Eleazer saw that he was troubled. He began, as every day, to wash his master's feet. The Vizier sighed and said, " Would that my own task were so simple."

And then, out of the heaviness of his heart, he talked to his slave and told him of the problem that was before the King.

Rabbi Eleazer said, " Perhaps God will show me a way to help the King. Take me to the King tomorrow."

That night the Rabbi Eleazer prayed to God. And he had a dream.

In the dream he saw the walls of the neighbouring city, and the river that flowed before them. At the edge of the river he saw a great stone, round as the earth. The stone moved, and rolled into the water. Where the stone had been, there was a hole.

In the morning Eleazer said, " Let the King take me aboard his ship, and I will show him what he must do."

The Vizier told the King of the request of his slave. " He comes from a far land, and is a wise man among his own people," said the Vizier.

" Is he a sorcerer? " said the King.

" He prays constantly to his God."

" Let him be brought before me," said the King.

When he was brought before the King, Eleazer said, " It is natural that you should doubt my wisdom, for I am only an unknown slave. I say to you that the enemy army is strong, and will destroy your army if you attack the walls of the city. If you would test my words, take from your galleys men who are already condemned to death, and put them in the first boat, and send them to attack the walls of the city."

The King did as Rabbi Eleazer advised. Convicts were chosen, and sent against the enemy. No sooner had they neared the wall than their boat was overwhelmed with a storm of arrows, spears, and darts of fire. Every man of them was instantly killed.

The King despaired, and cried, " What is there for me to do? "

" Wait until night," said Eleazer.

In the night, he guided the ship of the King through darkness across the water to a spot at the edge of the river where they found a great rock. This rock they rolled away, and the mouth of a tunnel was revealed. Rabbi Eleazer took a candle in his hand, and crept into the tunnel, and after him, one by one, came soldiers. Silently and slowly they went along the narrow, tortuous passage that was hewn through stone and digged through earth. At last they came up within the walls of the city. Thus a great army came up into the city, and attacked the enemies, and overthrew them.

When the King had captured the city he said to Rabbi Eleazer, " I will give you my daughter as your wife, and I will make you the highest man in the kingdom, after the King."

He placed Eleazer in a palace, and sent him slaves and riches. The princess who was given to him was beautiful and young.

But the Rabbi remembered that he was already married.

One morning when he sat at table with the princess she asked of him, " Why is it that you are not with me as a husband is with his wife? "

Then Eleazer said, " If you will promise not to reveal my secret, I will tell you."

She promised not to betray him, and then he told her that he was a Jew, and he told her of all the things that had befallen him.

Because the princess loved Rabbi Eleazer she took all of her jewels, and all of the gold that she possessed, and loaded a ship with her treasures. Then she said to Rabbi Eleazer, " Go on this ship, and find your way home."

He was joyous; day and night he sang his praises to the heavens.

But on the sea the King's ships overtook him.

Rabbi Eleazer cried, " Take the treasures from me, all the jewels and the gold. Leave me only with my God; he will guide me home."

Just then, God looked over all the earth, saying, " Where shall a man and woman be found who are worthy of bringing into the world an uncontaminated soul, the soul of Rabbi Israel? "

Elijah said to God, " There is Rabbi Eleazer, alone on the sea. He is worthy of being the father of such a son. In a village in Moldau, his wife has waited for him for seventeen years."

God called to the soul of Rabbi Israel, and showed him his father.

Rabbi Eleazer wandered homeward. He was naked and hungry.

On a path in a forest Elijah met him and said, " A son will be born to you who will be a light to all Israel."

In the little city of Okup, beneath the mountains, Rabbi Eleazer found his wife. Nine months after his return, she bore him a son, and they named the child Israel.

When the child had been circumcised, the mother died.

ISRAEL AND THE ENEMY

A STRANGE TALE, FILLED WITH HIDDEN MEANING,
TELLING HOW ISRAEL HELD IN HIS HAND
THE HEART THAT WAS THE KERNEL
OF DARKNESS

WHEN Israel was five years old, his father Eleazer was dying.

On the day of his death Rabbi Eleazer talked to his son. Eleazer was old, and the wandering that he had done over the earth had creased his body with pain. His eyes were weary, for they had stared many days upon thick clouds to see one instant of heaven. And now he was glad that his death was come.

He said to the boy, " My child, know that the Enemy will always be with you, he will be in the shadows of your dreams and in your living flesh, for he is the other part of yourself. There will be times when like a lightning-stroke you will pierce into his farthest hiding-place, and he will fade before you like a fleeing cloud; and there will be times when he will surround you with walls of darkness, and you will stand alone as upon a raft in the midst of a sea of night. But remember always that your soul is secure to you, for your soul is entire, and he cannot come into it; your soul is a part of God.

" Before you were born it was made known to me that God would always be with you, for within you there lives one of the Innocent souls of heaven. Then go fearless through your life on earth, do not be afraid of man, and do not fear the Enemy, for the highest power is in you."

After the death of Rabbi Eleazer, the Jews of the village cared for his child. Israel was sent to the cheder. But soon he found he could not bear to remain within the schoolroom; he would glide through the door and go into the woods, there he would remain all day long, walking under the trees, sitting among the flowers, or by the running river, absorbed with joy.

The schoolmaster would find him and take him back to the cheder. For a few days Israel would attend dutifully, but then again an urge would come into him, and he would run to the woods.

At last the schoolmaster lost patience with the boy, and left him to do as he pleased.

Then Israel lived joyously, he was brisk as a squirrel. He made himself a mossy place within a cave, and there he slept, or he slept in the branches of the trees, he lived on berries and fruit, he talked with the birds, he played with the untamed beasts, and sometimes he stood very still, and listened. So Israel grew.

When he was ten years old he came out of the woods to the village of Horodenka, and became a helper to the schoolmaster there. It was Israel's duty to go from one house to another early every morning, to wake the children and lead them to the cheder. In the evening he led them home.

Soon the Jews of Horodenka began to feel that the children were changed. They were like no other Jewish children. Often, they sang.

And this is how it happened that the children of Horodenka sang.

At dawn, the boy Israel went from house to house, calling to his followers. When he had gathered all his herd, he would lead them toward the fields, quite in the opposite way from the cheder. And then he would begin to sing. And the other children would also begin to sing; so they would go a long way through the fields and through the woods, going in a great circle until they came to the schoolhouse. In the late afternoon he would lead them again singing through the woods and the fields, they would come carrying green branches in their hands, with flowers woven in their hair.

Often they sang, " Praised be his Holy name, Amen! " For Israel knew no other song.

The voices of the singing children rose like arrows upward and broke against the heavy clouds of evil that the Enemy had spread over the earth. Each day the voices beat against the clouds, until they pierced into them. Soon a crack was made, and the voices reached the blue sky, and flew toward heaven.

Then the exiled and wandering Spirit called the Shechina, hearing the singing of the children, raised her head in the hope that the time had come when she might flow back into her Creator, and again be One with Him.

But Satan rose in furious hate and strode straight into heaven.

" Someone there below is interfering with my work! " he cried.

Elijah said, " It is only a band of children singing."

" Let me strive against the children! " Satan demanded of God.

And God nodded his head, saying, " Strive."

Then Satan went down to the earth.

He went to the wood where the boy Israel had

lived, there the Enemy crept over the ground, peering at every insect and crawling into the bosom of every flower; of insect and blossom he asked, "Will you carry my poison into the heart of the child Israel?"

But no living thing would turn against the child.

In that wood lived an aged charcoal-burner, who had been born without a human soul. His body lived, and ate, and slept. He did not know what was right and what was wrong. He was afraid of humans, and therefore hid himself in the forest; some people thought he was a sorcerer, and they feared him.

It was true that often at night a demoniac power would creep into the flesh of the old charcoal-burner; then he would feel himself becoming an animal. He would crouch, and sink onto his four paws. His limbs would become covered with fur. Then he would be a werewolf, and prowl under the trees.

Those who went late into the woods were often frightened by the werewolf's moan. But none had felt his teeth.

The charcoal-burner's simple heart shrank under the terrible urge that made him into werewolf; when he had howled his pain and shame, he would creep under a bush and lie there panting, unable to flee his self, until at last he slept.

So the Enemy found him sleeping.

Satan reached his hand into the breast of the sleeping creature, and took his heart out from his body. That heart Satan buried in the earth. And within the breast of the human werewolf he placed his own heart, that was the innermost kernel of darkness.

When Israel came at dawn with his singing children toward the forest, the Werewolf broke from the bush and rushed with snorting nostrils and teeth that flashed like knives toward the flock of children. The children screamed in fright, some fell insensible, some ran into the forest, some into the field, some clung to each other and cried, and some were taken with fever.

The Werewolf disappeared.

Israel called to the boys who had been with him, but they were run home crying.

Then the whole village was taken with fright. The children told of the terrifying wolf that had come out of the forest upon them, they shivered and whimpered and trembled, and some lay in the houses, sick with fright. The mothers and fathers said, " It is the fault of the boy who led them into the forest. We will not send the children with him any more."

When the other boys had run to their mothers and fathers, Israel went into the forest. He thought of the words his father had spoken to him, and he knew that what the other children feared, he need not fear.

He walked all morning in the forest.

Then he returned to the village, and went from one house to the other, speaking to the parents of the children.

" Let them come out with me again," he said. " No harm will befall them. A wolf ran by in the field, he was himself frightened of the children. Let them come with me again tomorrow, and you will see how they will no longer be frightened."

And the eyes of the boy were so earnest, and his

pleading was so strong, that the parents trusted him and said, " Come for the children in the morning."

At dawn of the next day Israel once more gathered his band about him. He spoke to them earnestly of many things, as a man speaks to his fellows. " Come behind me," he said, " and whatever happens, do not be taken with fright, do not run."

Then he began to sing, and the children followed him singing " *Yiskadal . . . !* "

He led them across the fields, to the very edge of the wood. There he stopped and said, " Remain here."

He went alone into the forest. At once the Beast emerged from behind the trees, and came toward Israel.

The boy saw the Beast becoming larger, he saw the Beast grow until his back was a scowling cloud arched beneath the heavens, and his paws clutched the whole earth, and the bloody vapour that issued from his mouth covered the rising sun.

But the boy was not afraid. He walked straight forward, going into the very body of the Werewolf, and nothing stopped his steps. He came to the dark glowing heart of the Beast. Round and shining like a black mirror it lay before him; all of the knowledge and all of the desire of the world were drawn into its gloomy depths, and all of the evil and all of the untruth in the world were reflected outward from its surface, reflected with such a black and universal brilliance of hatred that only his universal love of God saved the boy from being blinded, and drawn into the mirror, to become a part of its evil.

That black heart was given into his hand.

He closed his fingers tightly over it, he held it fast.

But then he felt it palpitating within his hand, shivering and jerking like a fish out of water, he felt the blood drop from it, and he knew the immeasurable pain that was in that heart: pain that began before time began, and would endure forever.

Then he took pity, and gave freedom to the heart.

He placed it upon the earth; and the earth opened and swallowed the black heart into itself.

Israel looked around, and saw that he was alone. He went and found his band of children and led them on to the cheder.

At the close of the day, townsfolk found the charcoal-burner lying dead under the bushes in the woods. A smile of simple innocence was on his face. His eyes were closed.

Then, they did not understand why they had ever feared him, saying he became a werewolf at night in the woods. For in death he was like a child.

From that day forward the children of Horodenka ceased to sing as they went after Israel through the fields; they began to be like their fathers, and the fathers of their fathers, with their heads bowed between their shoulders.

THE BOOK OF MYSTERIES

IN THIS STORY WE LEARN HOW THE BAAL SHEM TOV
RECEIVED THE BOOK OF ADAM, AND OF THE
FRIGHTFUL END THAT CAME TO THE
SON OF RABBI ADAM

WHEN the children of Horodenka ceased to sing, Israel was no longer content to remain in that place. He wandered again, and returned to the town of Okup, where he had been born. There he became the watcher of the synagogue.

The desire for knowledge came into him; and the joy that was given him by flowers and beasts in the forest was no longer sufficient. His mind was afire and thirsty, but his thirst could be quenched only by those waters that had cooled for ages deep in the deepest wells of mystery, and the fire within him was of the sort that burns forever, and does not consume.

The innermost secrets of the Cabbala were for him, and they were only as stars of night against the sun. For to him would be revealed the Secret of Secrets.

The boy lived in the synagogue. But since the time for the revelation of his power was yet far away, he did not show his passion for the Torah to the men of the synagogue. By day, he slept on the benches, pretending to be a clod. But as soon as the last of the scholars blew out his candle and crept on his way toward home, Israel rose, and took the candle into a corner, and lighted it, and all night long he stood and read the Torah.

In another city the Tsadik Rabbi Adam, master of all mysteries, waited the coming of his last day. For in each generation one is chosen to carry throughout his lifetime the candle that is lighted from heaven. And the candle may never be set down. And the soul of the Tsadik may not return to eternal peace in the regions above until another such soul illuminates the earth.

Rabbi Adam was even greater than the Tsadikim who had been before him. For in the possession of Rabbi Adam was the Book that contains the Word of eternal might.

Though Rabbi Adam was not one of the Innocent souls, he had led a life so pure that this Book had been given into his hands. Before him, only six human beings had possessed the knowledge that was in the Book of Adam. The Book was given to the first man, Adam, and it was given to Abraham, to Joseph, to Joshua ben Nun, and to Solomon. And the seventh to whom it was given was the Tsadik, Rabbi Adam.

This is how he came to receive the Book.

When he had learned all Torah, and all Cabbala, he had not been content, but had searched day and night for the innermost secret of power. When he knew all the learning that there was among men, he said, " Man does not know." And he had begged of the angels.

One night Rabbi Adam arose from his sleep. He walked into a wilderness. Before him stood a mountain, and in the side of the mountain was a cave. And that was one mouth of the cave, whose other mouth was in the Holy Land. It was the cave of the Machpelah, where Abraham lies buried.

Rabbi Adam went deep into the cave, and there he found the Book.

All of his life Rabbi Adam has guarded the secret of knowledge. Gazing into it, he had grown old, and he had come to see with the grave eyes of one who sees to the end of things.

And when he saw himself growing old, he began to ask, " What will become of my wisdom? "

Then he rose, and looked to the Lord and said, " To whom, Almighty God, shall I leave the Book of Wisdom? Give me a son, that I may teach him."

He was given a son. His son grew, and became learned in the Torah. The Rabbi taught his son all that there was in the Torah. And he said, " My son learns well." He began to teach his son the Cabbala. His son was sharp in understanding. But when the boy had learned the secrets of the Cabbala, he asked no more. Then the old heart of Rabbi Adam was weary and yearned for death. " My son is not the one," he said.

Night after night Rabbi Adam prayed to the Almighty that he might be relieved of the burden of knowledge. And one night the word came to him, saying, " Give the Book into the hands of Rabbi Israel, son of Eleazer, who lives in Okup."

Rabbi Adam was thankful, for now he might give over his burden, and die. He said to his son, " Here is one book in which I have not read with you."

His son asked, " Was I not worthy? "

" You are not the predestined vessel," said Rabbi Adam. " You would break with the heat of the fluid."

Then he said to his son, " Seek out Rabbi Israel, in the city of Okup, for these leaves belong to him. And if he will be favourable toward you and receive you as his servant and instruct you in his Torah, then count yourself happy. For, my son, you must know that it is your fate to be the squire who gives into the hands of his knight the sword that has been tempered and sharpened by hundreds of divine spirits that now lie silent under the earth."

Soon Rabbi Adam died. His son did not think of himself, but thought only of fulfilling the mission his father had given into his charge. He deserted the city of his birth and, taking with him the leaves of the Book, went in search of that Rabbi Israel of whom his father had spoken.

The son of Rabbi Adam came to the town of Okup. He wished to keep secret the true reason of his coming, so he said, " I am seeking a bride. I would marry, and live my life here." The people of the town were delighted, and felt greatly honoured because the son of the Tsadik, Rabbi Adam, had chosen to live among them.

Every day he went to the synagogue. There he encountered scholars, and holy men, and rabbis. He asked their names of them. But he did not meet with any one called Rabbi Israel, son of Rabbi Eleazer.

Often, when all the others had gone from the synagogue, Rabbi Adam's son remained studying the Torah. Then he noticed that the boy who served in the synagogue also remained there, he saw that the eyes of the boy were bright with inner knowledge, and that his face was strained with unworldly happiness.

Rabbi Adam's son went to the elders of the house of prayer and said to them, " Let me have a separate room in which to study. Perhaps I shall want to sleep

there sometimes when I study late into the night.
Then give me the boy Israel as a servant."

" Why has he chosen the boy Israel, who is a clod? "
the elders asked.

Then they remembered that Israel was the son of
Rabbi Eleazer. " He has chosen him to honour the
memory of his father, Eleazer, who was a very holy
man," they said.

When the boy came to serve him, the son of Rabbi
Adam asked, " What is your name? "

" Israel, son of Eleazer."

The master watched the boy, and soon came to feel
certain that this was indeed the Rabbi Israel whom
he sought.

One night he remained late in the synagogue. He
lay down on a bench, and pretended to be asleep. He
opened his eyes a little, and he saw how the boy Israel
arose and took a candle and lighted it, and covered
the light, standing in a corner and studying the Torah.
For many hours the boy remained motionless in an
intensity of study that the rabbi had known only in
his father, the Tsadik Rabbi Adam.

All night long the boy studied. And when the sun-
rise embraced his candle flame, he slipped down upon
the bench, and slept.

Then the rabbi arose and took a leaf from the holy
book his father had given him, and placed the leaf on
the breast of Israel.

Soon the boy stirred, and sleeping reached his
hand toward the page of writing. He held the page
before his eyes, and opened his eyes and read. As he
read, he rose. He bent over the page of mysteries, and
studied it, and his whole face was aflame, his eyes

glowed as if they had pierced into the heart of the earth, and his hands burned as if they lay against the heart of the earth.

When full day came, the boy fell powerless upon the bench, and slept.

The rabbi sat by him and watched over him until he awoke again. Then the rabbi placed his hand upon the boy's hand that held the leaf out of the book. The rabbi took the other pages of the book, and gave them to him, saying: " Know, that I place in your hands the infinite wisdom that God gave forth on Mount Sinai. The words that are in this book have been entrusted only in the hearts of the chosen of the chosen. When no soul on earth was worthy to contain its wisdom, this book lay hidden from man. For centuries it was buried in unreachable depths. But always there came the time for its uncovering, again it was brought to light, again lost. My father was the last of the great souls to whom it was entrusted. I was not found worthy of retaining it, and through my hands my father transmits this book to your hands. I beg of you, Rabbi Israel, allow me to be your servant, let me be as the air about you, absorbing your holy words, that otherwise would be lost in nothingness."

Israel answered, " Let it be so. We will go out of the city, and give ourselves over to the study of this book."

The son of Rabbi Adam went with Israel to live in a house that stood outside of the town. There, day and night, they were absorbed in the study of the pages that contained the words of all the mysteries.

THE BOOK OF MYSTERIES

Israel was as one who feeds on honey and walks on golden clouds. His soul swelled with tranquil joy, and his heart was filled with the peace of understanding. Often, he went with the leaves of the book into the forest, and there, the words of the book were as the words spoken to him by the flowers and by the beasts.

But the son of Rabbi Adam was eaten by that upon which he fed, and yet his hunger grew ever more insatiable. The grander the visions that opened before him, the greater was the cavern within himself. And he was afraid, as one who stands on a great height and looks downward.

Each day, his eyes sank deeper, and became more red.

Rabbi Israel, seeing the illness that was come into his companion, said to him, " What is it that consumes you? What is it that you desire? "

Then the son of Rabbi Adam said, " Only one thing can give me rest. All that has been revealed to me has set me flaming with a single curiosity, and each new mystery that is solved before me only causes a greater chaos in my mind, and a greater hunger in my heart."

" What is the one thing that you desire? "

" Reveal the Word to me! "

" The Word is inviolate! " cried Rabbi Israel.

But the son of Rabbi Adam fell on his knees and cried, " Until I see the end of all wisdom, I cannot come to rest! Call down the highest of powers, the Giver of the Torah Himself, force Him to come down to us, otherwise I am lost! "

Then the Master shrank from him. He said, " The
hour has not yet come for His descent to earth."

His companion was silent. He never pleaded with
Israel again.

But each day Rabbi Israel saw his face become
darker, and his body become more feeble. The hands
were weak, and could hardly turn a leaf.

Rabbi Israel was torn with pity for his companion.

At last he said, " Is it still your wish that we name
the Giver of the Torah, and call Him to earth once
more? "

The son of Rabbi Adam remained silent. But he
lifted his eyes to the eyes of Rabbi Israel. They were
as the eyes of the dead come to life.

" Then we must purify our souls, that they may
reach the uttermost power of will."

On Friday, the two rabbis went to the mikweh,
where they bathed in the spring of holy water. From
Sabbath to Sabbath they fasted, and when they
reached the height of their fast they went again to
the mikweh, and purified themselves in the bath.

On the second Friday night they stood in their
house of prayer. They called upon their own souls
and said, " Are you pure? " Their souls answered,
" We have been purified."

Then Rabbi Israel raised his hands into the darkness, and cried out the terrible Name.

The son of Rabbi Adam raised his arms aloft, and
his feeble lips moved as he repeated the unknowable
Word.

But in the instant that the word left those lips, Israel
touched him and said, " My brother, you have made

an error! Your command was wrongly uttered, it has been caught by the wind, it has been carried to the Lord of Fire! We are in the hands of death."

" I am lost," said the son of Rabbi Adam, " for I am not pure."

" Only one way is left to us," cried Rabbi Israel. " We must watch until day comes. If one of us closes an eyelid, the evil one will seize him, he is lost."

Then they began to watch. They stood guard over their souls. With their eyes open they watched. And the hours passed. They stood in prayer, and the hours passed.

But as dawn came, the son of Rabbi Adam, enfeebled by his week of purification, and by the long struggle against the darkness of night, wavered, his head nodded, and sank upon the table.

Rabbi Israel reached out his arm to raise him. But in that moment an unseen thing sped from the mouth of Rabbi Adam's son, and a flame devoured his heart, and his body sank to the ground.

THE SECRET MARRIAGE

HERE ARE TOLD THE MARVELLOUS DEEDS OF RABBI
ISRAEL WHILE HE WAS STILL A SAINT
IN SECRET

AFTER the death of his companion, the Master forsook the house where they had lived and studied together. Israel returned into the forest. There, for the length of a day, he sat by a stream and watched the flowing water.

And he said to himself, " Shall I go among men, or shall I remain in the forest? "

He thought, " For what purpose shall I go among men? I am the master of all knowledge. There is nothing that I can learn among men." He built himself a cottage, and he lived in the forest.

Yet he knew that he must go among men and help them; for what else might be done with the power that had been given him! " Mankind will contaminate the truth," he said. " Let me remain a while longer where I am." And he waited for a sign.

Near the forest was a field where a shepherd came every day to pasture his flock of sheep. The shepherd was an aged Jew.

He came to know the young man who lived in the woods. One day he said to him, " Why do you live by yourself? I have a daughter, I will give her to you for a wife."

Then Rabbi Israel was married to the shepherd's daughter. For a year's time he lived in the forest with her together, and in that time Rabbi Israel was happy on earth. He thought, " Perhaps I shall not ever have to return among men."

But when the year was over his young wife died.

Rabbi Israel got up and went out of the forest. In the city of Brody was a Yeshiva where many scholars sat learning.

He went to a hamlet near Brody, and he took work as a school-teacher, and he lived in the house of Rabbi Chayim. He did not let it be seen that he was a tsadik.

But Rabbi Chayim's wife, the rebetsen, was the sister of the great Gaon Maharim. And she saw that there was a strangeness in the face of the school-teacher who lived in her house. Then a thing happened that made her suspect he was a saint in hiding.

There was no place for Israel to sleep in that house except a small room in the garret. For many years the garret had been troubled by restless spirits who came during the night and ran over the walls, hammering, and hurling themselves against the floor, and making weird sounds of moaning. Rabbi Chayim and all the people in his house were afraid to go up into that room.

But Israel went there to sleep.

The rebetsen awoke during the night. She heard the weird moaning of the spirits. And all at once she heard the young man cry out, " Be still! "

From then on, there were no more sounds in the garret. This, the rebetsen remembered.

It happened that while Israel lived in that house, Rabbi Chayim and Rabbi Hirsch had to decide the judgment of the Torah in a very difficult case. Rabbi Hirsch was the father of Rabbi Gershon of Kuth.

A man in the city of Kuth had gone through Rabbi Chayim's hamlet, and had bought a horse. " When I reach home, I will send you the money, and you will send me the horse," he said.

And so he did. But when the horse came to him, it was lame.

The seller said, " The horse was well when it started to Kuth."

The buyer said, " It was lame when it came."

Then who was to bear the loss of the horse's lameness?

The two rabbis talked for many hours, but could come to no understanding. At last Israel, who sat listening in the room, said, " Did the horse draw a wagon on his way to Kuth? "

The man who had sold the horse said, " He drew a wagon."

" What was on the wagon? "

" It was loaded with logs."

" Then the logs belong to the lameness, give the logs also to the buyer of the horse."

Rabbi Hirsch was so pleased with the wisdom of this decision that he said to the young man, " Who are you? "

" I am a school-teacher in this village."

" You are the man whom God intended as the husband of my daughter. I will give her to you in marriage."

And he sat down at once to write the marriage contract.

But when Rabbi Hirsch asked of the Master,

" What is your name, rabbi? " the Master said, " Do not write down that I am a rabbi. Write only: Israel, son of Eleazer."

On his way home, Rabbi Hirsch died.

Afterwards Rabbi Gershon looked among the papers of his dead father. And there he found a marriage contract.

" Who is this Israel, son of Eleazer, to whom my sister is given in marriage? " he asked. But no one knew who that might be.

However, his sister said, " My father made the contract, and I will wait until my groom comes to claim me."

And still Israel did not go to claim the daughter of Rabbi Hirsch, but remained living in the house of Rabbi Chayim.

Once the rebetsen had to make a journey to the lord of the district. The way to the house of the paritz led through a forest that was infested with robbers. The rebetsen thought, " Whom shall I take with me to protect me from the robbers? " And she decided that no one would be better than the young man Israel, so she asked him to go with her in her wagon.

When they had come deep into the forest, Israel touched the rebetsen's arm and said to her, " Soon we will be stopped by a robber. Do not be frightened."

The woman felt that there was great power in the boy, but she did not know how truly great was his power. She said, " I have no money to give the robber, and he will kill us."

" The robber who will stop our wagon is one who

has murdered many people," said Israel. "But his measure is full, he will murder no more."

They rode on. The trees about them rose high, and the narrow road was a dark path under overhanging cliffs. It was dark as the inside of a cave.

The rebetsen said, "You are only a young boy. Could you kill a robber with your hands?"

Israel said, "I have the power of the Word."

All at once the horse stopped. The robber stood in front of them. He slapped the flat side of his sword against their legs. "Jews!" he shouted, "get out of the wagon! Part with your money or your souls!"

"We have no money," said Israel, "and you have no need of our souls."

At this reply the robber became black with anger. He seized the wheel as if he would wrench it from the wagon and break it over their heads. He began to mount the wagon. But before the robber could swing his foot upward, the Baal Shem Tov looked into his face and uttered a word.

The bandit stood petrified. He could not move his limbs. But he still could move his mouth, and he filled the air with his vile curses, flinging his oaths like thunderbolts upon them. He cursed them, and their fathers, and the fathers of their fathers, he cursed their children, and all the generations of the Jews, and he cursed their rabbis, with the blackest and most terrible of curses.

"Cease your blasphemy!" said Rabbi Israel. And he looked into the face of the robber, and once more he uttered a word.

At once the ground opened beneath the bandit,

and he sank into the earth up to his knees. Then a wild shout of terror and of rage hurled itself out of his throat. It was like the scream of iron grinding on iron. His arm, with the sword raised in the air, trembled like a beam that is strained to budge a heavy rock; the blood swelled in the veins of his face and of his arm; but with all his force he could not move his arm to hurl the sword at their heads.

Then he burst out more loudly than ever with curses that were more foul than the stench of hell.

Upon all the ancestors of the Jews he heaped his curses, and on Abraham, and on Isaac, and on Jacob, and upon the God of the Jews.

" Then it is time you were under the earth! " said Israel.

Once more he uttered a Word, and the robber sank slowly into the earth, his thighs were covered, and his belly, and his chest, and his shoulders were below the ground, then the earth closed over his throat and reached his chin, his cursing mouth was filled with earth, and the earth was in his eyes, his head was below the ground, and his outstretched arm, and his sword.

The rebetsen and the boy rode on their way.

When the wagon had passed out of the wood, Israel said to the rebetsen, " Now there is no more danger. I command you, do not tell any living soul what happened in the forest. You must not tell your husband, or your brother the Gaon Maharim. It is not yet time for my power to be known."

" What will be my reward for keeping silence? " asked the rebetsen.

" You will have peace in your grave."

For this, she agreed to keep silence.

Rabbi Israel said, " If ever you are disturbed in your grave, utter my name."

Many years later, when the rebetsen had long been dead, and Rabbi Israel was no longer a saint in secret, but was known among all Jewry as the holy man of Medzibuz, a plague came over that hamlet near Brody where the rebetsen had lived and died. Almost half of the people of the village died, and still the plague continued, and every day the peasants died like fleas.

Then the Christians looked toward the Jews and said, " It is their doing! " The peasants went to the priests and cried, " Only Jewish blood will save us! "

But the priests held them back, saying, " The Jews are not to blame. The Jews are also dying of the plague."

And for a time the peasants were satisfied.

But as the plague continued, and grew even worse, the peasants again rose against the Jews. They cried, " The Jews are an unclean people! They have strange ways: They have strange ways of burial. Even their dead are unclean. Their dead lie festering in the ground, and bring the plague upon us! "

An old man among the peasants, known for his wizardry, stirred them up, saying, " I know a cure for the plague. Come with me at night, to the graveyard of the Jews. All who come, bring spades! "

That night the peasants lighted torches. In the market place that was in the centre of their town they built a great pile of wood, and made it ready for burning.

Then they chose ten men amongst them, and sent them with the wizard to the cemetery of the Jews.

" Where is the holiest of their graves? " said the wizard.

No one knew.

Then they went and seized the keeper of the cemetery, and they dragged him into the graveyard. " Where is the holiest of your graves? " they cried. " Tell, or you yourself will be used to light the pyre! "

They brandished their torches over his head. The Jew was frightened, he ran in terror and threw himself down on the grave of the rebetsen. " Save me, holy rebetsen! " he cried.

The peasants threw him aside. And they placed themselves around the grave of the rebetsen, and began to dig.

At first, she became restless at the sound of their digging. She stirred in her coffin. But she thought, " Perhaps they are digging another grave near by."

But as the digging came closer to her coffin, and she felt the tight earth above her loosen, she became frightened, and wondered what was happening.

Suddenly a spade struck upon her coffin.

Then she remembered, and cried out loud: " Rabbi Israel! "

In the morning, the wizard and all his followers were found lying dead upon her grave.

After the Master of the Holy Name had revealed his power to the rebetsen, he did not remain long in her house. He decided that he would go and claim his wife. Then, changing his rabbinical garments for the short jacket and heavy boots of a peasant, Israel started out on foot for Kuth. He came to the city, and went directly to the house of Rabbi Gershon.

Rabbi Gershon was deep in study over a difficult problem in the Torah, and he did not notice that a man had come into the room. But when he had finished reading he looked up and saw that a peasant was standing there. He was not pleased with the man. He cried out, " What do you want? "

Rabbi Israel, speaking gruffly like a peasant, said: " I have come to take my wife."

" Who is your wife? Who are you? "

" Your sister is my wife. I am Israel, son of Eleazer."

" How can it be that my father pledged my sister to a peasant? " thought Rabbi Gershon. " She could marry into the richest of families, or she could be wedded to the most celebrated of rabbis! " Yet he did not wish to distrust the wisdom of his dead father. He looked upon Israel, and asked him:

" What is your profession? "

" I am a lime-burner. I work in the hills."

" No! " cried Rabbi Gershon. " It cannot be that you are the man! "

Rabbi Israel showed him the contract.

Then Rabbi Gershon called his sister. " Here is the man to whom your father betrothed you," he said. " You see that he is a peasant, an ignorant lime-burner. It cannot be that your holy father betrothed you to an ignorant boor. Let us send him out of the house."

But the girl said, " My father made a marriage contract for me, and I will keep it."

" I cannot have a peasant in this house," said Rabbi

Gershon. " Break the contract! I will pay him money, and he will go away."

Israel said, ".I have come for my wife, not for money."

" Break the contract," said Rabbi Gershon, " or marry him and go out of the house! "

" I will marry him and go away with him," said the woman.

Israel took his wife with him high into the Carpathians. Near the village of Zabie he built a cabin for them to live in. He worked as a lime-burner, and his wife helped him. Thus they earned a scant livelihood. But sometimes Israel would take dry bread in a sack, and go away into the hills. He would remain by himself all week long; before the Sabbath he would return home. He would remain at home during the Sabbath, and during the following week again take bread and wander among the high hills, contemplating God.

In those mountains, too, there were many robbers. They had their forts in the forests, and they sallied out in bands to attack wealthy travellers on the roads.

Once, hidden among the trees, a number of these bandits saw the form of a man who walked on the ledge of a mountain-peak. A chasm lay between the cliff he walked upon and the next mountain.

The man seemed absorbed in thought. He did not look where he walked.

" He will surely walk off the cliff! He will fall into the chasm! " the bandits cried to one another.

They could not move, but watched him.

THE PEASANT'S BRIDE

Then they saw the two mountains move together, and close the chasm between them.

The Master stepped safely from one peak to the other peak. And when he had passed, the mountains separated behind him, and were as they had been, with the chasm lying between them.

When the robbers saw this happen they said one to another, " He must be a holy man! "

Then they ran toward him and said, " Be our judge! "

Rabbi Israel answered, " If you will promise never to injure a Jew, I will be your judge."

They agreed.

" I live in the cabin near Zabie," he said. " When you need a judge to decide your quarrels, come to me."

Once two of the thieves quarrelled over the division of their spoils. They came to Rabbi Israel in his cabin and asked him to say which of them was in the right. Together, they had stopped a carriage. One of them had held the horses. The other had beaten a fat merchant and robbed him of his coffers. " I nearly killed the merchant! " he bragged. " The better share of the money belongs to me! " But his companion declared that the spoils should be evenly divided.

The Baal Shem Tov said, " The second man is right. The spoils should be evenly divided."

The robbers accepted his decision, and returned to their fort.

But the killer was not content. After he had given his companion half of the money and jewels, he felt even more angry. When night came, he decided to revenge himself upon the Baal Shem Tov.

He took his knife, and went out on to the mountain. He went through the forest, and came to the Baal Shem's cabin. He opened the door, and went into the room. He saw Rabbi Israel sleeping.

The robber stood over the bed, and raised his knife to strike the sleeping Rabbi.

Suddenly the bandit was assaulted from behind. His arm was seized. He felt blows descend upon his shoulders. He was beaten with fists and with cudgels, he was beaten as by ten strong men, until he lay groaning on the ground. His head was covered with blood, and his body was blue with bruises. And still he saw no adversary. He thrust his arms wildly into the air, to catch at the bodies of those who were beating him, he tried to seize their sticks, he swung his arms all around him, but encountered only emptiness. And yet blows continued to descend upon him. Then he roared out loud with pain. The Baal Shem Tov awoke.

" What is it? " he asked. " Who is shouting here? " He looked, and saw the beaten highwayman, with his knife in his hand, lying on the ground. Then he knew what had happened.

Rabbi Israel got out of his bed, and went and fetched water, and washed the robber's wounds.

After having lived seven years in the Carpathians, Rabbi Israel and his wife returned to Rabbi Gershon in Kuth. Rabbi Gershon still believed that his brother-in-law was an ignorant peasant, and of no use in the world. He did not know what to do with him.

At last he thought of a plan. " Can you drive a carriage? " he asked of Rabbi Israel.

The Baal Shem said that he could drive.

" Often I have to go to the neighbouring villages to render judgements of Torah. You will drive my wagon."

So the Baal Shem Tov became a coachman for his brother-in-law. Once they went on a journey. When they had been riding for several hours, Rabbi Gershon fell asleep. Rabbi Israel was absorbed in contemplation, and forgot to guide the horse. The reins were slack in his hands.

A bull came charging along the road.

The horse was frightened. He jumped sidewise, and pulled the wagon into a ditch.

Rabbi Gershon lay bruised in the mud. " God has cursed me," he cried, " with a brother-in-law who is good for nothing! He can't even drive a horse! "

Then Rabbi Gershon decided that he could not abide to have his brother-in-law living in the same village. " What can I do with him? " he thought. " My sister will go with him wherever he goes. I cannot let them starve."

At last he decided, " I will set him up as a tavern-keeper."

So Rabbi Gershon enquired, and found that in a place named Itrup, near Kossow, there was an inn that could be bought very cheaply. It was a poor sort of place, as few travellers passed on that road; even an experienced tavern-keeper could barely earn his bread there.

Rabbi Gershon rented the tavern, and gave it to his sister and his brother-in-law.

There was very little to do in the tavern.

But the spot was a beautiful spot, lonely and wild, covered with trees and crossed with running streams. Behind the house the Master found a spring of water amongst a copse of trees. He set to work and carried stones, and built a mikweh around the spring; that purifying bath is there until this day. Near the mikweh he built a hut; when there were no people to serve in the tavern, he would retire to this hut, and remain there days long in meditation. When travellers came to the tavern, his wife would call his name, and he would come back to the house and serve his guests, make their beds for them, and bring them food and drink.

And still no one knew who he was, for he kept his power hidden.

Once Rabbi David of Klama, who was a friend of Rabbi Gershon, went through the country to gather gifts for the Chanuka feast. When Rabbi David came to Kuth, Rabbi Gershon said to him, " If you pass near Kossow, go to my brother-in-law's tavern at Itrup, and stay with him. And on your return, tell me the news of my sister."

" Is your brother-in-law a learned man? " asked Rabbi David.

" He is an ignorant peasant," said Rabbi Gershon bitterly.

Rabbi David came to the Baal Shem's tavern. Israel was not in the house, but was alone in his hut in the woods. His wife called to him, crying, " Israel, we have a rabbi for a guest! "

At once Israel ran into the house. He took a chicken, and killed it, and cooked it for Rabbi David. While Rabbi David ate supper, Israel went and made his bed.

And all through the evening, while the visitor spoke to the woman of the wisdom and fame of her father and her brother, Rabbi Israel sat quietly behind the oven.

At last Rabbi David went to sleep.

Then Rabbi Israel took the Torah, and began to read.

The Baal Shem Tov never slept more than two hours a night. Many nights he did not sleep at all, remaining awake over the Torah.

Now, as he pierced deeper and deeper into the pure realm of Wonder, the darkness that was about him gave way, for light seemed to stream from Rabbi Israel. He did not have a lamp for his reading, he read by the illumination that hovered about him where he sat.

And still the light grew, and glowed, and became bright as a bright flame. And Rabbi Israel sat in the midst of it; his soul was warmly bathed in the divine fire, his soul was filled with ecstasy.

Suddenly Reb David awakened. He saw the flame in the corner of the room. He leaped from his bed. He ran to call the tavern-keepers. But only Rabbi Israel's wife was in their bed. Rabbi David wakened her, shouting, " Quick, the house is on fire! "

But the Baal Shem's wife looked where there was light, and smiled and said, " If you believe there is a fire, put it out."

Reb David ran and got a pail of water and carried it to the oven. But as he was about to pour out the water, he saw Israel sitting there in the midst of the shining light, and he saw his ecstatic face.

Rabbi David did not understand everything. But he knew that this was a holy man. He was silent. He set the pail down noiselessly. He crept back to his bed, and closed his eyes. But all night long he could not sleep. He saw before him the ecstatic face of the Baal Shem Tov, as he sat bathed in the light of heaven.

When Rabbi David returned to Kuth, he went to Rabbi Gershon and said, " I stayed in the tavern of your brother-in-law."

" How is my sister? " asked Rabbi Gershon.

" She is well."

" And my brother-in-law, does he help her about the tavern? "

Rabbi David said, " Your brother-in-law is holier than you."

Rabbi Gershon laughed. " He can't even drive a horse," he said.

Rabbi Israel and his wife could not earn a living at the tavern. Rabbi Gershon did not help them any more.

" I will learn a simple way to earn a living," said Rabbi Israel. He went to Tluste, and worked for a butcher there, and learned to be a shochet. After that he returned with his wife to Brody, and became a shochet in Brody.

When Rabbi Israel was thirty-six years old, the voice of God came to him and said, " The time has come for you to reveal yourself."

Then the Master of the Name began to perform works of wonder.

THE BRIDE IN HER GRAVE

SOON the whole world knew of the wisdom and
power of the Baal Shem Tov. From all corners of
the Carpathians, followers came to him. Often he
went on journeys to far places to which the Will had
called him.

Once on a Wednesday night Rabbi Israel arose and
said, " I must go away for the Sabbath." He went into
the barn and harnessed his horse.

Several of his followers sprang after him and begged
that he take them with him. But he allowed only a
few of them to come into his wagon.

" Where will we hold Sabbath? " they said.

" In Berlin, in the house of a wealthy Jew."

Though they knew that with swiftest horses it took
more than a week to reach Berlin, they did not question the Rabbi, for the Master was not confined in
the bonds of time or of space.

The Baal Shem let his little horse walk slowly along
a byway all that evening, and at midnight the wagon
stopped before a tavern.

" Let us stay here tonight," said Rabbi Israel.

The tavern-keeper welcomed them into his house,
for he saw that they were holy men.

" Perhaps you will honour my house, and remain
over Sabbath? " he said.

But Rabbi Israel answered, " We must hold Sabbath in Berlin."

The inn-keeper looked at him, and did not understand. The Rabbi said, " On Sabbath eve there is to

be a wedding in the house of a wealthy Jew of Berlin, and I must be at the wedding in order to read the service, and bless the bride."

" You must have a wonderful horse," said the tavern-keeper, smiling.

" My little horse will get me there in time," said Rabbi Israel.

" In time for the Sabbath after this one," answered the inn-keeper, laughing. " Why, Berlin is farther than a hundred miles away. If you were to travel day and night, sparing neither man nor beast, you might arrive in time for the Sabbath after this one."

But his words did not trouble the Baal Shem Tov. Rabbi Israel turned to his followers and said, " You are tired. Let us go to sleep."

The tavern-keeper could not sleep that night. He lay awake wondering how the Rabbi would reach Berlin before the Sabbath fell. " This is Wednesday night," he said. " Tomorrow is a day, and Friday is only part of a day. No, I cannot understand it! " At last he said to himself, " I will tell him I have things to attend to in Berlin, and ask him to take me there."

When the Baal Shem Tov arose in the morning, the tavern-keeper ran to him saying, " Shall I harness the horse, Rabbi? "

" Not yet," said the Baal Shem Tov. " First we will pray. And after that, we will eat our breakfast."

" Rabbi," said the inn-keeper, " I have business to do in Berlin. Take me there with you! "

" When we start, come with us in our wagon," said Rabbi Israel.

The Master and his followers said the morning prayers, and after that they sat down around the table. They ate without haste, and while they ate they discussed the Torah. A problem of judgement arose, and they sat a long time discussing the problem.

Meanwhile the inn-keeper ran and dressed himself for the journey. When he was ready, he looked into the room where the Master sat with his students, and he saw them still absorbed in their discussions.

" Half the day is gone already! " thought the inn-keeper.

He heard Rabbi Israel's words. " Of every good deed we do, a good angel is born. Of every bad deed, a bad angel is born. In all the deeds of our daily life we serve God as directly as though our deeds were prayers. When we eat, when we work, when we sing, when we wash ourselves, we are praying to God.

" Therefore we should live constantly in highest joy, for everything that we do is an offer to God.

" And of those things that we do badly, work that we leave half finished, or thoughts that we leave uncompleted, malformed angels are born. Angels without heads, angels with no eyes, angels without arms, without hair, without feet. Therefore no deed should be left unfinished."

The inn-keeper thought, " If that is the way he travels to Berlin, the angel born of his ride will have perhaps the beginning of a toe, and nothing else."

But the rabbi and his students remained around the table, talking.

" I will tell you the story of a king," said the Baal Shem Tov. " There was a very wise king who had built for himself a strange and wonderful palace. In the centre of the palace was a room in which stood the throne. Only one door led into this room. All through the palace were passageways and halls and corridors that turned and twisted about and led in every direction, there were endless walls without openings, and there were more corridors and more passageways.

" When the palace stood finished, the King sent an order to all of his lords commanding them to come before him. He sat on his throne and waited.

" The lords came to the outside of the Palace, and stared in wonder at the confusion of corridors. They said, ' There is no way to come to the King! '

" But the Prince threw open the door saying, ' Here he sits before you! All ways lead to the King! ' "

Then Rabbi Israel added, " So we may find God."

In the afternoon, the Baal Shem Tov called the tavern-keeper.

" I will harness the horse at once! " said the tavern-keeper.

" No, not yet. First, we will eat the evening meal."

Then the Rabbi and his students sat down again, and ate largely and well.

As evening came, the rabbi himself went to the barn and harnessed the horse to the wagon. " Now we will go," he said.

The inn-keeper got into the wagon with them.

" At last I will see what manner of horse he has here," he thought. And he bound his cloth around his throat, for he thought, " A great wind will come because of our swift riding."

The little horse began to walk. At first, the tavern-keeper saw, they were going along the same road on which his tavern stoòd. Every house along the way he knew, and every tree. But as the darkness grew like sleep around his eyes, he was no longer sure where he rode. First, there seemed to be no more houses. Then there seemed to be no more people. And at last, there seemed to be no more trees. He was awake, he listened, and yet he could not distinguish the hoofbeats of the horse. The wagon moved silently through the darkness, smoothly as if floating on a surface of glass. The air was tender about his face, and there was a sweet odour in his nostrils.

He thought to himself, " Perhaps I am not here at all! "

Then he felt the chassid who sat next to him, in order to make sure that this was no vision.

" Where are we going? " he said.

" We are going to Berlin."

" But I do not recognize the road! "

The Baal Shem Tov said, " This is a short way."

All night long they rode, and the tavern-keeper saw no light of habitation, saw nothing but the stars in the velvet sky, and heard nothing but the voices of the chassidim as they talked of things in the Torah.

The Rabbi himself spoke of many wonderful things. He spoke of the prophet Elijah, who wanders about the world, and of how at the time of Redemption he would bring down Messiah, and then at last the Shechina, the Glory of the Living God, will cease her wandering, and unite again with Him.

" No man can hasten the coming of that day," said

the Master of the Word. "Even the mightiest of Words cannot bring down that day, as long as evil is among us."

Towards dawn, the inn-keeper began again to hear the hoofbeats of the horse. Then he felt the wagon jolting on a road. He saw trees, he saw houses. He saw that they were near a great city. And when they rode into the city, he saw that it was Berlin.

The tavern-keeper remembered that the Baal Shem Tov had said he was going to the house of a wealthy Jew to perform a wedding service. But now instead of driving to the street on which stood the houses of the rich, the Rabbi stopped before a humble guest-house and went in there with his students, and they said their morning prayers, and sat themselves down at the table.

The tavern-keeper wandered out into the streets. He was restless, and filled with the news of the marvellous ride he had taken, and he wanted to find someone to tell of the great wonder.

He came to the street of rich houses. Each house was a veritable palace. And one of these houses, he saw, was festooned as for a great feast. As the tavern-keeper stood before this house, the door opened and a young man came running out of it. Though he ran in great haste, he did not seem to know where to go, but turned first one way and then the other way. His face was terribly wrought in grief.

The tavern-keeper saw that the young man was wearing Sabbath clothes and new shoes. "He is certainly the bridegroom," he thought.

The bridegroom ran up to the tavern-keeper and said, "Where is there a doctor?"

The tavern-keeper seized his arm and cried, " Come, I know of a rabbi who works wonders! "

But the bridegroom stood still, repeating to himself. " Of what use will it be? She is dead."

The tavern-keeper could not contain himself, and cried, " The rabbi can do all things! He came a hundred miles in one night, to perform a wedding in Berlin! "

The bridegroom said, " The bride is dead."

The tavern-keeper said, " His powers are so great, he can surely raise people from the dead! Come, I will take you to him! " The bridegroom put out his hand, and the inn-keeper led him to the Baal Shem Tov.

" Tell me what has happened," said the Master.

" Today, I was to have been married," said the man. " Last night there was a great festival in the house of the bride. All through the feast, she was joyous, she danced, she was the happiest of all the people in the house. We danced together at our wedding feast. Then she went up to her room and slept. And this morning when she awoke and tried to rise, she fell to the ground, dead."

" Take me to the house," said the Baal Shem Tov.

They came to the beautiful house that was festooned for the wedding. They went through the ballroom where the feast had been held, they went up the stairway and came into the maiden's bedroom. There, dressed in a long white robe, lay the body of the bride. Beside her on the bed lay the wedding-dress that she had begun to put upon herself.

The Baal Shem leaned over, and looked into the

face of the girl. Then he said to the women who were in the room, " Dress her in her shroud." And he said to the men, " Dig a grave for her in the cemetery." And he said to the groom, " I will go with you to bury the bride. But you must do everything exactly as I order. Take her wedding-dress and her ornaments and her wedding-shoes, and bring them to the grave."

Then the women dressed the maiden for the grave. And when she was ready to be buried, they put her in a coffin. The bridegroom took her wedding-dress in his hands, and carried it with him as he walked beside the coffin.

Two grave-diggers had already made a hole in the earth. They straightened their backs, and prepared to climb out of the hole.

But the Baal Shem Tov called down to them, " Remain there, and do as I say. Let one of you stand at her head, and the other stand at her feet. Do not take your eyes from the face of the girl. And if a change comes over the face of the girl, I will give you a sign. Then lift her, and help her to rise."

They took the maiden as she lay in her shroud, and they put her down into the earth. They drew the cover away from her face, that the living might look the last time upon her. Her face was white as her shroud.

They did not throw earth over her body.

The Baal Shem Tov took his stick and leaned upon it, leaning over the open grave. His eyes looked into the face of the dead maiden. And all those who were there looked first at the face of the corpse, and then at the living face of the Baal Shem Tov. And as they watched his face, they saw that he had gone into another world. As they looked into his eyes, they could almost see what he saw in the other world. They knew that the Power was come over him, and that he was no longer among them. They saw his mouth move, and heard him speak words made of sounds they had never heard before. And none who were there by the grave could ever remember the Words that he had uttered.

Only the bridegroom kept his eyes upon the face of his beloved.

And after a long while, a shiver coursed through his back. For it seemed to him that he had seen a tinge of colour, delicate as the brush of an eyelid, pass upon her cheek.

In that same moment the Baal Shem Tov trembled with mighty force, as a man trembles who clutches with all his strength to hold back the wheels of a wagon that would break away and rush downhill.

Then Rabbi Israel straightened himself, and breathed freely. He made a sign to the two men, and they lifted the girl out of the grave. Her eyes were open. She looked to her bridegroom, and smiled.

" Dress her in her wedding clothes, and take her under the canopy," said the Baal Shem Tov. " All that has happened, forget."

With these words, Rabbi Israel started to walk away. But the groom ran after him and begged him to be the one to say the wedding service.

For the wedding, the feast was prepared, greater than ever before. And the joy in that house was unbounded, for the bride had returned from the dead.

Only, all day long, when they asked of her, " What happened over there? " she became confused, and answered in a bewildered way, " I do not know. I do not know who he was! "

When the couple stood under the wedding canopy, and the Baal Shem Tov began to read the wedding service, the bride started joyfully and cried out, " It is he! "

Rabbi Israel whispered to her, " Be still! " and he finished the service.

But when the blessing was over the bride could no longer contain her secret. She would not let the Rabbi go away. " It was he who brought me back from over there! " she said. " I know him by his voice! "

Then, as they sat to eat the wedding meal, the bride told of all that had happened.

The groom had been married once before. His first wife had been the aunt of this maiden, who was an orphan. The girl had lived happily in their house.

When the wife became sick, and knew that she was about to die, she called the girl to her bedside and said, " Promise me that you will never marry my husband. Otherwise, I cannot die in peace."

The maiden was afraid to make the promise, for she already felt stirring within her the love for her future groom. But because she could not deny the wish of the dying woman, she gave the promise that was asked of her.

THE BRIDE IN HER GRAVE

Then the woman called her young husband to her bedside and said, " I cannot die peacefully unless you promise never to marry my niece." In order that she might die peacefully, he gave her his hand and his word.

But after the dead woman was taken from the house, the man and the girl were left there together. Each day, they knew their love to be stronger. At last they could no longer restrain their love, and they agreed to marry each other.

On the morning of the wedding day, as the maiden arose to put on her wedding garments, the angry soul of the dead woman came into the house. She seized the soul of the girl, crying, " You have broken your sacred promise! Come with me! "

And before the Almighty she demanded the death of the bride.

As the bride was placed in her grave, her soul went up for judgement. The souls of the two women stood for judgement together. The soul of the first wife cried, " She has taken my beloved from me! "

And the soul of the maiden cried, " She has taken me from my beloved! "

At that moment, the Baal Shem Tov came up to the court of judgement. He placed himself between the two souls. " The dead have no right on earth! " he declared. " The right is with the living! "

He seized the soul of the girl, and drew it away from the soul of the dead woman. " The bride and groom are not guilty of wrong," he said. " The promise that they made was given against their wills. Their promise was made only to give peace to the soul of the dying woman. And now she must leave them in peace! "

The words of Rabbi Israel were judged to be right. And pronouncement was made, " Let the maiden's soul return to her body."

But the dead woman would not free the soul of the girl. She clung to the girl's soul with all her might.

" Let her go! " cried the Baal Shem Tov. And then he drew all his strength together and wrenched the soul of the maiden from the clutches of the dead woman's soul. " Let her go! Can't you see that the wedding canopy is waiting! "

That was when the bride returned to the living, and was taken out of her grave, and dressed in her wedding garments.

RABBI ISRAEL AND THE SORCERER

THE STORY OF THE TERRIBLE STRUGGLE BETWEEN RABBI
ISRAEL, MASTER OF THE HOLY NAME, AND THE
PARITZ WHO WAS IN LEAGUE WITH THE
EVIL ONE. AND HOW RABBI ISRAEL
CONQUERED

ONCE when he was riding on a journey, Rabbi
Israel passed a certain tavern. Although the sun
was still strong in the sky, the Baal Shem Tov said,
"We will stop at this place tonight."

The horses were turned around, the wagon drove
into the spacious yard, the Master descended and went
straight into the house.

It looked to be a prosperous inn serving the village
of a generous paritz whose lands were fat and whose
peasants drank well.

"Let us enter," said Rabbi Israel, and his students
followed him.

In the first room they saw a long table on which
there stood a great many bottles of fine wine. No one
was in the room.

"It smells of a feast," said Reb Wolf.

"We are just in time to celebrate a circumcision,"
said the Master.

They went into the next room. There they saw another table, covered by a fine white cloth, and on this
table were plates of roasted chicken, cakes, and all
sorts of delicacies. On a wide chair behind the table
lay an embroidered coverlet, and linen ready for the
circumcision. And there was no one in this room.

In the third room they found the inn-keeper, sitting
beside a small coffin.

The inn-keeper sat with his head bowed in his great thick hands. He stared into the tiny coffin. The coffin was empty.

The Baal Shem Tov said, " It seems you are preparing a feast for tonight, my friend."

The inn-keeper sighed.

" Is the child your son? " said the Baal Shem Tov.

The inn-keeper heavily nodded his head.

" Your only son? "

" My third son, and yet my only son," said the inn-keeper. " And with this one it will be as with the others."

" But this is a feast-day for you! " said the Baal Shem Tov. " You should be merry! Let me help at the circumcision, let me be the one to hold the child on my arms while it is offered for the rite."

" Willingly, master! " said the inn-keeper, for he saw that he spoke to a holy man. " It will be a great honour," he said. But his voice was without joy.

He looked into the coffin, and said, " Twice before, I have had a son born to me. And each time, on the night of the circumcision, we found the child dead. With this one it will be as with the others."

" Have you any enemies? " asked the Master.

" They are all good people about here," said the inn-keeper.

" Do you owe your paritz money? "

" The paritz is a fine nobleman, and very generous. Each time I have a briss, he sends me bottles of rare wine out of his own cellars, and he himself comes to the feast and watches the circumcision. See, today he has already sent many bottles of excellent wine. No, I have no enemies. If only I could have a son who would live, I would be very happy."

" Do not hold the circumcision tonight," said the Baal Shem Tov, " but tomorrow night. Now take me to see your son."

The landlord led the Master up a stairway and through a hall until they came before a heavily bolted door. The inn-keeper unfastened the three great locks that were on the door, and opened the portal. The room was dark. In the centre of the darkness they saw the shape of a little old grandmother sitting rocking a wooden cradle. When she heard the people coming into the room she spread her arms frightened over the cradle.

" I have brought a holy man," said the inn-keeper. At this the grandmother arose, allowing them to approach the child.

The face of the child was covered with a prayershawl.

" Why is the face of the child hidden? " said the Baal Shem Tov.

" That no evil eye may fall upon it," said the innkeeper. Then he lifted away the talith, and in the light that streamed through the cracks of the wall they saw the face of a beautiful child.

" He will be a learned rabbi," said the Master.

The hands of the inn-keeper trembled, and he said, " May God grant that it be so."

Then Rabbi Israel said to him, " I will tell you what to do, and you must do everything exactly as I say. Take the talith from the face of the child, though you may leave it over his breast. Take away the darkness. Put candles in the room, and keep them lighted.

Then call two young students of the Torah, and set them to watch here by your son throughout the entire night. They must watch that the candles are not extinguished. Let the students take a sack, and hang the sack with its mouth open behind the head of the child. If anything falls into the sack, they must close and bind it quickly. One of them will watch the sack, and the other will run and call me."

As the Master ordered, so everything was done. The circumcision was put off until the next day. Soon night came, and all those in the tavern went to sleep. Only, in the room where the child slept many candles burned, and two scholars sat by the cradle, studying the Torah.

Many hours passed. It was deep in the night.

Then a wind seemed to come from all around them creeping through the crevices in the walls. It made no sound, but it came into the room from all sides, chill as a moonlit stone, and the room became cold and clammy as the inside of a cave. The lights sank fainting, the flames fell and struggled to rise, and fell, and grew ghostly pale. The two students leaped up and hovered over the cradle. With their hands they shielded the two candles that burned by the head of the child. And the face of the infant boy shone steadily with beauty and with wisdom.

The students, bent anxiously over the cradle of the child, did not notice that a cat had come into the room. Silent, smooth as the wind it glided about the wall. Its eyes were white, glassy, chill as ice, yet as smoke rises from ice, so lines of blue fire flowed from the eyes of the cat.

The eyes shone whiter than the flames of the candles, but they were not as white as the radiant face of the sleeping infant who was already filled with the light of coming wisdom and holiness.

The cat crept all around the room, turning always nearer to the child in the cradle, and its twisted way was as the path of a wind on sand. Then it came near to the cradle, behind the cradle it stood crouched ready to spring.

Its glossy sides sank and widened with its breathing; otherwise the cat was motionless.

Cold fire came out of its eyes.

The flames of the candles shrank low like backs beaten under whips.

The cat sprang.

But when its eyes encountered the light on the face of the sleeping child, it was as if the cat had been stricken backward in midair, it fell heavily into the open sack.

The students started at the thud. Instantly they remembered the command of the Master. One of them seized the mouth of the sack, twisted it tight and tied it close. The other ran and called the Baal Shem Tov.

The cat rolled and struggled and clawed in the sack. Again and again it leaped upward and fell back. Winds whirled in the room. The candle-lights were whipped high one instant, and shrank quivering the next.

But when the Baal Shem Tov came into the chamber the lights rose and flamed steadily. The cat ceased to jump upward, and lay in a jerking heap at the bottom of the bag.

The Baal Shem Tov felt the sack, and he began to laugh softly. " Bring me a stick," he said.

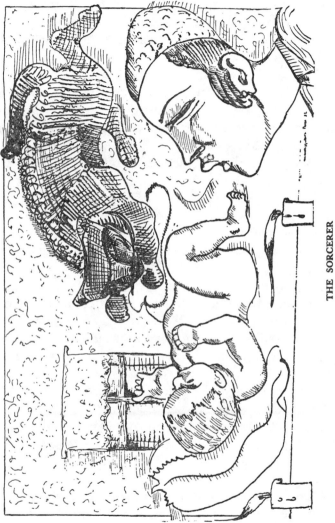

THE SORCERER

They ran and brought him his heavy stick. Then he took the stick and began to beat the cat in the bag. The cat howled, and the Baal Shem laughed, and danced with the stick, and belaboured the sack with all his might.

The inn-keeper came running.

" Here, dance a little at your son's feast! " said the Baal Shem Tov, and he handed the stick to the inn-keeper, and the inn-keeper went at the sack and beat it with all his might.

What was in the sack ceased to jump and to struggle; it lay still.

The Baal Shem Tov said, " Open the window."

Then he unbound the sack, and he went to the window and shook out the sack, and they all heard the cat fall to the ground. It crept away on its belly.

The next day the inn-keeper made a greater feast than he had ever made before. He celebrated the circumcision of his son. Musicians came, and all the Jewish families from miles around came to be joyous over the circumcision, and the peasants came and drank and sang and danced.

The Baal Shem Tov held the child on his arms, and the child was circumcised.

But in the midst of the festival, the inn-keeper said, " It is strange that the paritz has not come to the tavern. Every other time, he came himself to wish the child good luck."

Then Yashka, a peasant who worked in the house of the paritz, said, " The paritz is sick today."

The Baal Shem Tov laughed softly, but the inn-keeper did not notice his laughter. The inn-keeper said to his wife, "We will send a honeycake to the paritz, and tell him of the briss of our son."

So they took a large honeycake and wrapped it in fine white cloth. The Baal Shem Tov said to the inn-keeper, " Do me a favour. Let me carry the cake to the paritz."

" With the best of my heart," said the inn-keeper, and he gave the present to the Master.

The Master went with the cake and came to the great dwelling of the paritz. He was led into a spacious hall; raised at one end of the hall was a carven bed, and on the bed lay the paritz. His arms were all covered with bandages, and the flesh of his face was blue.

" I have brought you a honeycake, your excellency," said the Baal Shem Tov, and he came to the side of the bed.

Then they looked into each other's eyes. The eyes of the paritz became white and cold and glinted like pieces of ice. Rabbi Israel laughed a low soft laugh.

Then the paritz said, " Well, you gave me a good beating."

Rabbi Israel became stern, and said, " The inn-keeper is an honest man and serves you well. You have no right to persecute him."

" He is a Jew," said the paritz.

" From now on," declared the Baal Shem Tov, " know that he is protected by a power greater than your power! "

" Your magic can never be as potent as my sorcery! " cried the paritz. " Last night you caught me unawares. Come into open strife with me! Come to a test of strength, and I will show you who is more powerful! "

"If I defeat you," said the Baal Shem Tov, "you will put aside your sorcery forever, you will hold no more traffic with demons, you will stay locked in your own place and leave my people in peace."

"If I defeat you," said the paritz, "I will destroy you altogether!"

Then the Baal Shem Tov said, "I shall go now. In a month's time you will be well, then I shall return, and hold a contest with you."

When a month had passed, Rabbi Israel, accompanied by nine of his students, came to the castle of the paritz.

"I am ready," said Rabbi Israel.

Then the paritz ordered that his courtyard be prepared for the terrible contest. A great platform was built for him, and upon the platform a huge furnace was constructed, and all of his dark engines of destruction were set around the furnace.

"Now make your preparations," said the paritz to Rabbi Israel.

But the Baal Shem Tov needed no engines of destruction. "I will stand on the naked earth," he said. And he chose a spot for himself, facing the platform of the sorcerer. He made a great circle upon the earth. Within that circle he traced a smaller circle. And within the smaller circle he stationed himself, while his students stood around him.

All of the peasants from the countryside, for a distance of many miles, came to see the Jew who would stand against the paritz. The courtyard was filled with peasants, and the roofs of the houses of the village were covered with people.

But the few Jews who lived in that place closed

themselves in their huts, and shrank against the walls, and prayed.

Then the paritz began his terrible works of wonder.

He brewed a powerful fire within his furnace. And when the fire flared so hot and fierce that no man could approach within his own length of the furnace, the paritz himself went up and flung open the furnace door.

Out of the flames there charged wild beasts, lions and tigers without number! They leaped from the fire, springing to the very edge of the circle that the Master had made on the ground. And they prowled all around the edge of the circle, snarling, and tearing the earth with their claws.

But the Baal Shem Tov called out a tiny prayer, and the beasts shrank as from the onslaught of slashing swords.

Then the paritz conjured out of the air a second charge of beasts whose bodies were covered with iron scales and whose heads were armed on all sides with tusks of steel. And these beasts flew against the circle made by the Master. The outer circle wavered and bent.

" Quick, repeat the prayer! " said the Baal Shem Tov to his students.

With one voice they repeated the call.

At the same moment, Rabbi Israel made a cabbalistic sign upon the beasts. Then the circles he had made did not break, but became as a pair of immense and powerful jaws that seized the charging beasts and crushed them into nothingness.

But the paritz laughed and said, " I have only begun! "

He called up a third army of beasts more horrible than the second; and he called up a fourth army; wave upon wave his horrors came and charged upon the circle of the Master, they snarled, they roared, they tore the ground until clods flew all about the heads of the Baal Shem Tov and his students, they stamped and bellowed and raged, they vanished and came in renewed numbers, but they did not pierce the circle.

Night came. But the paritz said, " I have not finished."

He called upon the beasts of the night.

Then the forest was pierced with white staring glassy eyes that floated low and high, the forest was filled with chill clammy winds, with shrill long whistling sounds; from under the earth came groanings, and the ground heaved as when innumerable dead strive to break out from their graves; and all the air resounded with the clanking of loose bones.

The Baal Shem Tov called out a Name, and all was still, and day came.

On the second day and the second night the sorcerer continued his battle, but his forces were of no avail, and on the third day he began to feel his weariness; his strength was going from him, while he saw that the Baal Shem Tov and his nine students remained standing sturdy and untouched.

Then the paritz resolved to bring up the most foul and terrible, the last of his powers in an attempt to overcome the Rabbi.

The paritz went up to his furnace, and opened the fiery door. " Bring logs! " he called. And the peasants brought great logs, and filled the furnace to its utmost, and the blast of its furious heat was so great that the onlookers fled from the courtyard.

And when the fire had reached the topmost pitch of violence, the paritz himself walked into the midst of the flames. There he summoned Satan to him. And the two demons of evil stood in the flames, and laid all their powers together for a supreme assault that would consume the Master.

At last their forces were in readiness. The sorcerer came out of the furnace. He seized a living swine, and opened its belly, and hurled the entrails upon the ground.

Then the earth broke open into a black gap that was filled with crawling things, that was like a festered wound. And out of that hole there heaved a swarm of wild swine. Endless as the waves of the sea they came in numbers spewed upward from that hole, and out of the maw of each boar there hissed a charge of fire.

Enraged they burst against the circle of the Master. They broke the first ring, their fire burned the earth, they swarmed all around the Master and his nine students who clustered within their last retreat. Then the beasts attacked that last circle made by the Master. Their flames ate at its borders, and its borders gaped with holes.

The Master raised high his arms. His students separated from about him, they stood back and looked upon his face, and they saw that his face was charged with the terrible light of heaven. His face was bathed in pure white fire that was stronger and more consuming than all the fire of all the armies of evil.

Then the Master opened his mouth to utter the Holy Name, and as his mouth formed the Word, and the Word went forth, the evil fire dried in the maws of the beasts, their bodies faded to nothingness, the wound in the earth closed and was healed, and the forest was transformed with peace.

Then the paritz came down from his place. He fell on his knees outside the circle of the Master, and he said, " Your power is greater than mine. Look on me, and annihilate me with a glance of your eye."

But the Baal Shem Tov said, " I will not destroy you." And he commanded, " Stand up."

The paritz arose.

" Lift your eyes," said the Baal Shem Tov.

The paritz lifted his eyes to the sky.

Then all who were assembled there saw two eagles come swiftly flying; the birds swooped downward, they came directly over the head of the sorcerer, then each bird reached with his beak, and so the two eagles took out the two evil eyes of the paritz.

TWO SOULS

THE MYSTERY OF TWO SOULS THAT WERE SEPARATED, AND HOW RABBI ISRAEL BROUGHT THEM TOGETHER WHEN THEY SUFFERED RE-BIRTH ON EARTH

THE Baal Shem Tov said, From every human being there rises a light that reaches straight to heaven. And when two souls that are destined to be together find each other, their streams of light flow together, and a single brighter light goes forth from their united being.

At the beginning of every year, among the hundreds of pilgrims who made their way to the cottage of the Baal Shem Tov in Medzibuz, there always came a very small woman, poorer than the rest, and humble. She was the wife of a wood-cutter in a distant village. Each year she came on foot to Medzibuz, and bowed her small head before Rabbi Israel. And each year she would say to him, " I pray to God to give me a child. Rabbi Israel, if you too will say a little prayer for me, the Almighty One will surely send me a child."

But Rabbi Israel knew that no soul was yet allotted to be born through her, and each year he said to her, " Go home and wait."

Year by year he watched her growing older, he saw how she became bent with toil, and how the lines on her small face deepened with the pain of her unfufilled desire.

But one year he said to her, " Go home. This year, a child will be given you."

And then, during five years, the little woman did not come to the Baal Shem Tov. He knew that she had a child, and that it was difficult for her to make the journey with the infant.

But on the fifth year he saw her coming. She led a child by the hand. And she was become so bent and shrunken that she seemed smaller than the young boy who walked beside her.

She said to the Rabbi, " God has blessed me with a child, but I cannot keep this child."

Rabbi Israel put his hand on her hair, and said, " Is this not the son for whom you prayed so many years? "

" He is flesh of my flesh," said the old woman. " But his soul is not kin to my soul. I cannot look into his eyes, for they are the eyes of a stranger. Rabbi, he is a gentle boy, and obedient, and good, but he is not of my poor world. I tremble before his wisdom."

The Baal Shem Tov looked at the boy. The child was beautiful, with a large head, and great black eyes that were filled with mysterious wisdom.

" I am afraid of his eyes," said the mother. " Rabbi, when he was born, and he opened his eyes for the first time and looked into my eyes, it was as if I had been pierced by two hot beams. Rabbi, I was terribly frightened. I knew at once that he was not my child. And ever since then, I have been frightened."

" Leave the child with me," said Rabbi Israel.

Then he raised the boy in his house; and as the boy grew, he began to study in the books of the Law, and he learned so quickly and so perfectly that he was soon the best of all the scholars in the house of the Baal Shem Tov.

Many wealthy Jews, hearing of the intelligence and beauty of the scholar, came to the Baal Shem Tov seeking to make a marriage contract for their daughters with the boy Issaschar.

" It is not yet time for him to marry," Rabbi Israel would say to them.

But when Issaschar was fully grown, Rabbi Israel called his trusted follower Rabbi Wolf and said to him, " I will give you the name of a certain man in a village far from this place. Go there and find the man. Ask him to give us his third daughter as a wife for our young Issaschar."

Then Rabbi Israel told Rabbi Wolf of certain signs by which he would know the girl. He also told him her name, and her age, and how she would seem.

Rabbi Wolf journeyed to the distant village, and began to ask among the richest houses there for the man whom he sought. But the man was not known among the wealthy, nor was his name known in the synagogue. Then Rabbi Wolf went to all the places where men gathered, old and young, and enquired for the man he sought. But he did not find him.

At last Rabbi Wolf despaired of fulfilling the command of his Master. He wandered alone on the road. Not far from the village he saw a poor man who was coming to the town, carrying on his back a great basket filled with vegetables. The man was bent under the weight of the basket.

" Tell me your name," said Rabbi Wolf to the gardener.

The man spoke his name, and the messenger knew that this was the man he sought.

" Set down your basket," he said.

The man set down his basket.

" I have been sent to seek you by Rabbi Israel, the Baal Shem Tov. He asks if you will give your third daughter in marriage to our young scholar Issaschar."

Then a smile came onto the face of the gardener, and he laughed with joy.

" Why shouldn't I? " he said. " My house is filled with daughters! They run around barefoot, they quarrel over each crust of bread. And where will I ever get money to provide each of them with a dowry! "

" There is no need of a dowry," said Rabbi Wolf. " Besides, my Master will provide the wedding, and give the bride wedding clothes, and furnish a home for the bride and the groom."

The gardener was overjoyed. " For it just happens," he said, " that the daughter for whom you ask is the quietest of all the girls. She does the work about the house, and she comes out to help me in the garden. She is good and gentle. And yet, sometimes, she is as a stranger among us."

Then Rabbi Wolf told him the name of his daughter, and gave him other signs, to make sure that she was the one.

On the next day, the little old Jew and his daughter started with Rabbi Wolf for Medzibuz.

When they arrived, they were received with great honour by Rabbi Israel. The girl was given good clothes to wear, and shoes to put on her bare feet.

For the wedding festival, the Baal Shem had sent to the little village where the mother and father of Issaschar lived, and the aged couple had come to see the wedding of their son.

And now a great feast was prepared, and the canopy

was made ready. The Baal Shem Tov himself read the service of the marriage, and blessed the husband and wife.

When the wedding was concluded, Rabbi Israel sat at the head of his great table. On his one side was the father of the girl, and on his other side was the mother of the boy. And the girl and the boy were there, and all of the chassidim sat around the table. Then Rabbi Israel said, " I will tell you a story."

They knew by his voice that this was no idle story he would tell, and all became quiet, and listened.

The boy and the girl put their hands together, and listened.

Then the Baal Shem spoke. " Long ago in a distant land there was a King who passed his days in worry and his nights in torment because he had no heir. Year after year went by. He called to him every wise man and every sorcerer in his kingdom, but their wizardy was of no avail. He sent to all the corners of the earth, and brought wise men and sorcerers to his court, and they tried with all their might to force the Supreme Will to send down a child to the King. But none of their efforts availed.

" At last the most learned of the sorcerers said to the King, ' I have thought of a way.'

" The King said, ' Tell me what it is, and I will do it, though I have to destroy my kingdom in its accomplishment.'

" Then the sorcerer said, ' In your land there are many Jews. These Jews have a powerful God. Send out a command forbidding the Jews to worship their God, forbidding them on pain of death to indulge in any of the practices of their religion until a son is born to the King. Afterwards, if a son is born to you, you may allow them to return to the practices of their religion. And say in your command that if any Jew is found worshipping his God while a son is not yet born to the King, he shall be put to death.'

" The King agreed, and sent out a declaration that the Jews were forbidden to read in their holy books, or put on phylacteries, or wear the prayer-shawl, or circumcise their male offspring, or to perform any of the rites of their religion, on pain of death, until a son was born to the King.

" Then darkness and bitterness came over all the Jews of that land. Many fled the kingdom. Others pretended obedience by day, but at night crept into houses of prayer that they had digged under the earth, they hid themselves in secret places, in graveyards, in forests, and there they worshipped their God with feverish intensity, begging that they be saved from the commands of their King.

" When sons were born, they might not be circumcised, for when the officers of the King found a child had been secretly circumcised, they seized the child and cut him in two with their swords. Thus many of the children of Israel were slaughtered, and the Jews of the land were filled with grief.

" The angels on high saw the suffering of the Jews. Then the purest choir of souls that entour the throne of the Almighty had pity on the Jews, and begged God to send the King a son. But the Almighty would not yield, or change the order of the going down of souls.

" At last one soul, purer than all the rest, the soul of a Tsadik who had been freed forever from earthly bonds, and who had won his place in the highest rings of heaven, came before God and said, ' I offer to suffer *gilgul* and take earthly form again. Let me go down and be born as a son to that King, so the Jews of his land may be free once more to worship the unutterable Name.'

" God consented. Then the soul of the Tsadik went down to earth, to be born as the son of the King.

" But when the child was born, the King, in the greatness of his joy, forgot all about the Jews, and as no Jews were permitted to come into the palace, there was no one to remind him of their suffering. The laws against them were not withdrawn, and just as before they were forbidden to worship their God.

" The prince grew. He became a beautiful boy, and he surprised everyone with his quickness in learning.

" The King took care that the prince should have no desire unsatisfied. The boy was surrounded by every luxury known to man, and provided with every delicacy. A hundred slaves bowed to the slightest movement of his fingers.

" But the prince seemed to take no joy in luxury. He desired only wisdom. The most learned men in the kingdom were brought to the court to become his teachers, but the boy was so quick to learn that before he was six years old he had sucked dry of their knowledge all the wise men in the land. Then the King sent abroad once more, and brought scholars and magicians to his court. But none of them could quench the thirst that was in the prince. Soon he knew all the languages of men, and all the sciences of men, and yet he was sad, seeking some unknown thing.

"All day long he wandered by himself in the garden.

"His father the King would come to him and say, 'Why are you unhappy?'

"The boy would answer, 'Bring me a sage who can teach me happiness.'

"The King was more grieved than he had been before the child was born. He did not know where to find such a sage.

"At last the King heard his people talking of a learned man who had appeared in the city, who spoke in the streets and in the market-place, and whose words were filled with marvellous wisdom.

"The King sent out messengers to seek for that man, and after many days he was found in one of the small streets of the city. 'Will you teach my son wisdom?' the King said to him.

"The aged man was willing to become the teacher of the prince. But he asked only one thing. 'Give me a chamber,' he said, 'that shall be for me alone. Let no one be permitted to come into that chamber. And during one hour of each day, let me retire into that chamber, and be alone. Let no one disturb me, or spy upon me in that chamber.' This wish the King granted, and the stranger became the teacher of the prince.

"The prince was happy with his new master. There seemed no depth of wisdom which he had not plumbed. They were together all the day long, and spoke of things on earth, and below, and above. Often the prince woke at night, with a question on his lips, then he asked for his teacher to come and sleep in the same room with him, and so they slept in the same room.

" The prince did not know why it was, but he loved the aged stranger. He loved to walk with him in the garden, to sit by his side at table, to listen to his voice.

" But during one hour every day the prince was unhappy.

" He asked the aged man: ' Where do you go, when I cannot find you? '

" Then the teacher said to him, ' I have a closed chamber, and for one hour each day I am alone there.'

" The boy could not bear to think that his beloved friend should have a secret from him. He did not wish to spy upon his teacher, but at last, like a child, he could withhold himself no longer. One day he hid behind the curtains of his master's private chamber. He saw the master come into the room, and stand before the altar, and put a fringed shawl over his head, and wind phylacteries about his arms. Then the boy stepped from his hiding place and said.

" ' Here I am.'

" The old man was not angry with him, for he loved the boy. But he feared what might come of this knowledge, and he said to the boy, ' No one must know of what you have seen here.'

" The boy said, ' Why do you do these things? '

" The aged man said, ' I am a Jew.'

" The boy said, ' In all the times when you have been with me, I have felt at peace because you were at peace. But in this chamber I have seen you joyful, I have never seen you so joyful.'

" The aged man said, ' Here, I worship my God. And I worship my God with joy.'

" The prince wanted in every way to be like his teacher, and he said, ' Teach me to worship your God.'

" ' It is forbidden,' said the old man. Then he explained to the prince how the King had forbidden the Jews to practice their religion until a son should be born to him. ' With many others, I fled the kingdom,' he said. ' But when I heard that there was a prince in the land, I returned. Nevertheless, the Jews are still forbidden to worship their God; therefore I put on my prayer-shawl and my phylacteries in secret in this room, and no one must know what I do.'

" After that, in the same hour every day, they retired to the room of the teacher, and the boy learned to read in the books of the Torah. He learned quickly, and the Tsadik's soul that was in him became joyous. At the end of that hour each day it become more difficult for him to tear himself from his studies. ' Let us spend all of our time studying the Torah,' he said.

" ' Then we must go away from here,' said the sage. And he made a plan. ' We will escape at night, and go to a far city where we may freely worship our God.'

" In the midst of the night they wrapped their holy books in bundles, and went out of the palace and fled.

" The old man took the prince to a distant city where he was known and honoured. There the boy grew; soon he became celebrated among the rabbis for his wisdom. ' He will be a Tsadik,' they said of him.

" But when they spoke in that way of his perfection,

the boy became sad, and a vast yearning and loneliness came over his face. For he had already knocked on the innermost door of heaven, and the door had remained closed to him, while a hand had shown him the blot that was upon his soul.

" One day the sage took the prince to visit the chiefest of the rabbis of that city. As they came into the house of the great rabbi, his daughter saw the young prince, and her soul quivered. The prince looked on the girl, and he felt that she would be the end of his loneliness.

" Afterwards the girl went to her father and asked of him that he speak to the teacher of the young scholar. The chiefest of the rabbis came to the sage's house and said, ' Your young scholar is the worthiest of the young men. Let him become the husband of my daughter.'

" So the two children were married. So true was the love of their souls, that at the moment of their marriage a single light streamed upward to heaven, and lighted the whole world.

" But on the night of their marriage the boy said to his wife, ' Dear one, there will be times when my soul will leave my body, my body will lie as dead, and you will be stricken with fear. At those times you must not call anyone, nor be alarmed, but must remain sitting by my side, and wait silently until my soul returns to this body.'

" She answered, ' Beloved, I shall do as you say.'

" So they lived together in that city, and they were happy in their love.

" But once, at night, the soul of the prince left his body, and was away for a very long time. The bride sat by his body, and held his hand, and waited. The hand became cold as stone. The face became white as snow. The brow shone in the pallor of death. From moment to moment she leaned her head to his heart, and she heard how the heart beat ever more faintly.

" The bride was frightened, she wanted to run from the house and call people to help her, but she remembered the words of her husband, and sat by his side, and waited.

" At last, when dawn came creeping, a flush of colour returned with the first flush of light to the cheeks of her husband. Soon she felt warmth in his hand. Then she knew his soul had returned to his body. But his body was very weak, and he did not rise from the bed.

" ' Know,' he said, ' that this night I pierced to the highest of heavens, and stood before the Unnameable Presence. And I asked what would become of me. My soul was born in sin, all my youth I was raised in luxury in the palace of a king, while my people suffered. And for the youth that I passed in ignorance and in luxury, and for that I lived uncircumcised, there is a stain upon my soul, and my soul will be forever prevented of attaining perfection. Then, there is only one thing that I may do. I may consent to immediate death. Afterwards, my soul must be reborn of a pure but humble woman, and the first years of my life must be passed in poverty, for only in that next incarnation may I attain perfection. Beloved, I must depart from this life. Beloved, let me go.'

" Then his wife said to him, ' Only on one condition will I consent that you give yourself to death. Let me die with you. Let me be reborn when you are

WEDDING

reborn. Let me come back to earth, and as your wife be one with you again."

" He said, ' May it be so.'

" They lay down to death together, and their souls went forth in the same breath. For timeless ages their souls strayed in the darkness where there is no boundary of space. And at last the soul of the boy returned to earth to be born as the son of a little old woman who lived in poverty in a wood-cutter's hut on the mountain. And the soul of the girl returned to earth to be born as the daughter of a poor gardener, the father of many daughters.

" Then, far from each other, the two children grew. And in each child there was a sadness and a yearning for it knew not what, and each child, though gentle and good at home among its people, was as a stranger in its world.

" And so all the days of their childhood and youth were a seeking for they knew not what, their eyes looked with hope toward each new soul, and yet they saw into endless darkness, until they forgot what they awaited. But know, my friends, that these two souls at last have found each other, and are come together here as bride and bridegroom on this day."

Then the Master was silent. And all those who sat in the house felt a sweet joy arise within them, and they looked up with eyes that seemed to greet the wanderers of eternity, and all of their faces seemed to be lighted by a single mighty flame that rose heavenward.

THE STANDING SHEEP

ONCE, when the Baal Shem Tov was on a journey, Sabbath overtook him on the highway. He stopped the wagon, and went out into the field to perform the services that welcome the coming of Sabbath, and to remain there until the Sabbath was ended.

On the field, a flock of sheep were grazing.

When the Baal Shem Tov raised his voice and spoke the prayers that welcome the Sabbath as the coming of a Bride, the sheep rose upon their hind legs, and lifted their heads in the air, and stood like people listening.

And so they remained in wrapt attention for two hours, all the while that the Baal Shem spoke.

THE MAD DANCERS

ALREADY the voices of opponents were raised against the Baal Shem's teaching, for many rabbis could not understand his ways. Some said of him that he dishonoured the Sabbath with singing and freedom, some said that his ways and the ways of those who followed him and called themselves Chassidim were truly the ways of madmen.

One of the scholars asked of the Baal Shem, " What of the learned rabbis who call this teaching false? "

The Baal Shem Tov replied, " Once, in a house, there was a wedding festival. The musicians sat in a corner and played upon their instruments, the guests danced to the music, and were merry, and the house was filled with joy. But a deaf man passed outside the house; he looked in through the window and saw the people whirling about the room, leaping, and throwing about their arms. ' See how they fling themselves about! ' he cried, ' it is a house filled with madmen! ' For he could not hear the music to which they danced."

RABBI ISRAEL AND THE HORSE

HOW RABBI ISRAEL, THROUGH UNDERSTANDING THE
LANGUAGE OF BEASTS, SAVED A TORMENTED
SOUL

OFTEN when he had to ride to a distant village Rabbi Israel would stay overnight at the house of the tavern-keeper, whose child he had saved from the evil eye of the paritz. Usually Rabbi Israel journeyed in his own little wagon; but it sometimes happened that he rode upon the stage-coach. The driver was named Chayim, and Chayim was fond of a drink.

Just before the tavern there was a very steep hill. When a wagon had to go up that hill, the horses sweated and the drivers swore and lashed their whips, and often those who sat in the wagon had to get out and help the horses drag it up the hill. But Chayim was like no other driver on the road. Chayim made his horses run up the hill, one two.

Only, before he performed this feat, Chayim needed a drink. Every time he came to the hill he stopped his horses, took a bottle out of his pocket, and swallowed a good drink for himself. Then he said to those who were in the wagon, " You had better do the same! " and he offered them the bottle. And Rabbi Israel would drink with him, for when men drink together they are friendly to each other and their joy is purest worship.

When the horses reached the top of the hill, Chayim needed another drink, and for this he would go into the tavern.

So every day Chayim drank in that tavern, and every day he owed the tavern-keeper more money.

" Some day I'll pay you! " he swore, " even if I have to pawn my soul! "

" We live only once! " Chayim would say. " Here's life! " And who could deny him?

Once when he was very joyous it happened that Chayim fell off his wagon and broke his neck and died.

Then all the Jews in that region were sorrowful; for there had never been so fine a driver as Chayim on the road. But the tavern-keeper was more sorrowful than any of the others, for Chayim owed him a great deal of money.

A few years later Rabbi Israel passed that way, and stopped with his old friend the tavern-keeper. Rabbi Israel came in his own wagon, and as was his custom, himself took care of his horse. At night he went out to the stable to feed his horse, and while he was in the barn he looked around him to see how many beasts the tavern-keeper had in his barn this year, whether fewer or more than before. And he saw that the tavern-keeper was prospering. He looked at one horse after another, he patted their flanks, and rubbed them with his palms. Then, as he understood the language of birds and beasts, he talked with them for a moment.

As he went along the stalls, he saw one little horse that was trying to come near him, pulling at his halter, and tossing his head up and down, and calling to the Rabbi.

Rabbi Israel went up to him, and passed his hand along the nose of the horse. Then he listened to the horse.

Afterwards he went and got oats out of his own sack, and gave them to the horse. And he got a pail of fresh water for the animal. Then he went into the tavern, but quickly returned to the barn. And this time he poured a little whisky from a bottle into the horse's pail.

When the Rabbi was back in the tavern he said to the landlord, "Do you know what, sell me that little horse you have in your barn, the one that is smaller than all the others."

The tavern-keeper answered, "Master, you know that I would gladly give you anything I possess. Take one of the other horses. Take two of the other horses. They are fine horses, and worth more than the small one."

"But it is just that little horse that I would like to have," said the Baal Shem Tov. "I have taken a fancy to him. Tell me, why would you rather give me two better horses, than sell me this one."

"It is only because of the hill," said the tavern-keeper. "You know the steep hill there in front of the house? He is the only horse that can pull a wagon up that hill all by himself. When he comes to that hill, he pulls like three horses instead of one."

Rabbi Israel softly laughed. And he said no more about the matter.

But an hour afterwards, he said to the tavern-keeper, "Tell me, are you prospering here?"

"With God's help," said the man.

"Do many people owe you money?"

"Well here and again they owe me money. When they can, they pay."

" Let me see the papers you have from those who owe you money," said the Baal Shem Tov.

The tavern-keeper did not understand what he could want with such things; nevertheless he went and brought the papers. The Baal Shem Tov looked at them one after another.

At last he said, " Will you give one of those debts over to me? "

" Take whichever one of them you choose," said the landlord.

Then Rabbi Israel took one of the papers from the bundle, and returned the others to the inn-keeper. The inn-keeper looked at the name on the paper the Rabbi had chosen, and he laughed out loud. " What do you want with this one! " he said. " Can't you see it is the debt of Chayim the coach-driver? He has been dead for three years, Rabbi! You'll never get any money out of him! "

" Nevertheless, I want you to give his debt over to me," said the Rabbi.

The tavern-keeper handed him the piece of paper. The Baal Shem Tov took it and tore it to bits and threw it into the fire.

" Go and look to your little horse in the stable," said the Baal Shem Tov to the tavern-keeper.

The man scratched his head, because he could not understand what was happening. But he took a lantern, and he went to the stable and looked for his little horse, the one that pulled up the hill like three horses pulling together,

The little horse lay dead.

Rabbi Israel said to the tavern-keeper: " Do you remember, now, that Chayim swore he would pay his debt to you? When he died, his soul could not come into heaven until he had paid his debt. So his soul entered into the horse, and in order to work out his debt he laboured like three horses together. Tonight he begged me to help him. He spoke to me, and I saw that it was time for his soul to be released."

The tavern-keeper marvelled more than ever at the wisdom of Rabbi Israel.

THE BURNING TREE

REB BARUCH, the scribe of Klaminke, tells that once in the midst of winter he rode with the Baal Shem Tov and several of the Rabbi's followers. Evening came. Rabbi Israel said, " Let us stop the wagon and go down and say the evening prayer."

Ice was falling against their faces. Some said, " It is too cold, we will freeze. Let us drive on more quickly, until we come to a house."

But the Master said, " Stop."

So the horses were halted. Rabbi Israel got down from the wagon. And one by one the chassidim got down after him. They were numb with cold. They could hardly stand on their feet.

Rabbi Israel went up to a tree that stood by the road. He touched the tree with his hand, and the tree burst into flame.

The chassidim came close to the tree, they formed a circle around it, and warmed themselves, and prayed the evening prayer.

Then they got into the wagon and rode on.

Reb Baruch says that he turned in the wagon and looked behind him, and saw that the tree continued to burn, and was not consumed.

THE WATER–SPIRIT

HERE THE STORY IS TOLD OF THE REVENGEFUL LAKE
THAT WAS ANGRY BECAUSE OF THE HIDEOUS SIN
THAT HAD BEEN THROWN INTO IT, AND HOW
RABBI ISRAEL SAVED THE SINNER'S SON

IN old Constantine there lived a cousin of the Baal
Shem Tov whose name was Reb Shmerl. And Reb
Shmerl was a sinner. He committed one sin after another. "What does it matter if I sin twice or sin
twenty times?" he said. "At the end of the year I
take all my sins and drag them down to the edge of
the water. I throw them into the lake, and that is the
end of them. And for the new year, I am a clean man."

So Reb Shmerl lived from year to year. And each
year the sea became a little blacker, because of the
sins he threw into it, and each year the bundle of sins
that he brought down to the edge of the water was
greater than that of the year before.

"The lake is close to my house!" he laughed. "I
have not far to carry my sins! Let there be a few more
in the bundle!"

But his wife said, "It is because of your sinning that
God does not send us a son." His wife was a holy
woman, a Tsadcket.

Reb Shmerl said, "Do you really think that is so?"
And she said, "Yes."

Then he said, "Well, perhaps it is really so." And
he thought no more about it.

And that same year, he committed a sin that was
uglier than all the sins he had ever made. This sin
was huge and shapeless, it was like a great sponge
oozing and dripping with mud. He could hardly find

a place to hide it until the end of the year, when he would throw it into the lake. He put it into the basement of his house. But there, the sin seemed to grow larger, to expand, until the basement was not high enough to hold it, and the mud of the sin began to squeeze itself through all the cracks and to ooze into the rooms of the house, and to fill every corner of the house with its damp crawly smell. At last, New Year's day came. Reb Shmerl took hold of the sin in both his arms, and by pulling with all his might managed to squeeze it through the door of the house. He got it out of the house, then he pushed and rolled it down to the lake.

" There! " he said as it sank into the water. " I'm rid of that! "

The sea was angrier than ever. It hissed and shook itself and heaved itself upward trying to hurl the sin back to the shore. Yet all of its rebellion was of no use, for it had been ordained when the waters were created that on New Year's they had to receive into themselves all of the sins of men, and cleanse them. So at last the lake became quiet, and set to work to cleanse the sin. But the deed of Reb Shmerl was not forgotten; the waters waited for vengeance.

Reb Shmerl saw that his hair was becoming grey, and his wife had passed her best years, and still they had no children. At last he said:

" I will go to my cousin Rabbi Israel. They say he performs wonders for every stranger that comes to his door. As for me, I am a member of his family! "

He came to the Baal Shem Tov in Medzibuz and he said, " Cousin, I am growing old, and I would like to have a son to live after me."

Rabbi Israel talked with him for a while, and remembered Shmerl's wife, the holy Tsadeket. At last the Master said, " Go home. I can only promise you that you will have a son."

" But what more did I ask! " said Reb Shmerl; and he began to dance with delight, but the Baal Shem shook his head.

The Baal Shem Tov's promise was fulfilled. Before the year was over, Shmerl's wife gave birth to a strong and beautiful boy. The father was so proud that he said, " I will go at once on another journey to Rabbi Israel, and thank him for what he has done for us."

Then he came again to Medzibuz, and entered the cottage where the Master sat studying. The Master looked up at him, and the Master's eyes were filled with deep compassionate sorrow. When Reb Shmerl looked into the eyes of Rabbi Israel, all his joyous words faded from his lips. He did not know why, but he wanted to weep. Suddenly he was crying like a child.

Then the Baal Shem Tov said to him, " Your son will grow into a strong and happy boy. But on his thirteenth birthday he will go into the water and drown."

Reb Shmerl cried like a woman. He fell on his knees to Rabbi Israel and begged, " Help me."

Everyone knows that the Baal Shem Tov was not fond of weeping. But he remembered that the man's wife was a Tsadeket. Now he lifted up his cousin and said, " The sea is angry with you because of that terrible black sin that you threw into it. There is only one way to save your son. On his thirteenth birthday, he must be kept away from the water."

Reb Shmerl thanked him with all his heart. Reb

Shmerl was filled with joy, his tears were forgotten. "That is not difficult at all!" he said. "On his thirteenth birthday, I will keep him away from the water!"

And he was ready to run off on his way back home.

But Rabbi Israel called to him and said, "Do not think it is so easy to remember. You will surely forget the danger that awaits your only son!"

Reb Shmerl said, "How could I forget!"

But the Baal Shem Tov, who saw even then how it would be with Reb Shmerl, said, "Before you go, I will give you a sign that will help you to remember the day. When you awaken on that day, you'll begin to dress yourself, and you'll draw two stockings onto the left foot, and then hunt everywhere for the stocking for your right foot. Warn your household that on the day you cannot find your stocking, something terrible will happen."

Reb Shmerl thanked him, and returned to Constantine. And he thought, "What a foolish thing the Rabbi said about the stockings!" So he didn't tell anyone about it.

The boy grew. He was stronger than any of the other boys in old Constantine. He could run faster, and his eyes could see further, and his hands could move more quickly. As for learning, he had only to look upon a page, and he remembered it.

But most of all things, he loved to swim in the water. He would dive to the very bottom of the sea, and there he would swim around, seeking beautiful stones. These he would bring home to his mother.

He learned to stay under the water for many minutes. The fishes would come in and out of his hands, playing with him.

As Reb Shmerl saw his son growing up so strong and big, he forgot all about the gloomy warning of the Baal Shem Tov. By the time thirteen years had passed he did not remember Rabbi Israel's prediction at all. And he prepared to celebrate the Bar Mitzveh of his only son with a great feast.

On the morning of the boy's thirteenth birthday, Reb Shmerl was awakened by the heat of the sun on his face. It was hotter than it had ever been before, he thought. He felt his whole body burning as if it were inside a furnace.

He began to dress himself.

He felt very uncomfortable. He felt he had not slept enough. He was angry because the sun had awakened him. And his head hurt with the heat.

He drew a stocking onto his left foot. And then he stopped to wipe the sweat from his body. And then, without looking what he was doing, he drew his other stocking onto his left foot. Then he looked for the stocking for his right foot, He looked among his clothes, and did not find it. He looked under the bed, and did not find it. He got up, and began to hop around the room, hunting for another stocking. He stumbled into the next room, and blundered all over the house, knocking over chairs, and hurting his knees, and falling, and balancing himself against the wall. And he muttered and cried with anger, because the day was very hot, and he could not find his other stocking.

He shouted and woke his wife.

" What is the matter? " she said.

" Where is my other stocking! " cried Reb Shmerl.

Then his wife arose, to see what was troubling him. He pointed to his leg, and muttered, " Someone has hidden my other stocking! I can't find my other stocking! "

The Tsadeket looked at her husband, and saw that he was wearing two stockings on one foot, for when he went jumping around his stockings had become loosened.

" Look, Shmerl! " she laughed, " you have them both on your left foot! "

He looked, and he saw. Then suddenly he remembered the words of Rabbi Israel. And he began to tremble. And he ran to the room where his son slept. The boy was not in his bed.

Reb Shmerl ran to the door. He looked through the doorway, and saw the boy already on his way to the lake.

Reb Shmerl shouted to his son, " Come back! "

But the boy answered, " It's hot! I want to swim in the water! "

" Come back! " cried the father.

But the boy would not come back.

Then, with one foot covered and the other foot bare, Reb Shmerl began to run after his son. The boy ran swiftly. The father saw him nearing the lake.

" Master, help me! " cried the father. And he named the name of Rabbi Israel.

Then the boy tripped over the root of an old tree. Before he could rise to his feet again, his father was at his side.

" Come home with me," said the father.

He led the boy to the house, and placed him in a room, and locked the door.

It became very hot. The boy cried, and beat on the door. " Let me go to the lake! " he screamed. " I want to go to the lake! "

But they would not open the door.

At last he begged them only to let him out of that room, because it was so very hot in there. But they would not let him out of the room. After that, he begged them to give him a pan of water with which to cool his body, but Reb Shmerl was afraid to give him even a glass of water to drink.

And after several hours the boy became worn out, and weak, and fell to the floor and slept.

Many people went to bathe themselves in the sea that morning. As the sun rose higher, the lake became filled with swimmers. They laughed, and sported in the cool water.

When the sun reached the middle of the sky, and blazed angrily down on the earth, then nearly every soul in old Constantine was bathing in the lake.

At exactly the hottest moment of noon a disturbance began in the water. Ripples grew in circles around a certain spot near the shore, as though a stone had been thrown into the water there. The ripples widened, and became a sworl. And out of the midst of the sworl, a hand appeared, reaching up from the water. Then a second hand appeared. The two hands rose upward, reaching. The full arms appeared, hairy with greenish seaweed. And after the arms came long floating seaweed hair. A head rose from the water, and a neck, and shoulder, and the upper part of a body, all hairy with greenish seaweed. Then the head turned slowly from one side to another, and the arms reached outward, and the eyes looked into the faces of all the bathers.

The mouth moved. The voice was harsh and deep. " One is missing! " it shouted angrily.

And the head sank back into the sea.

When the sun had gone down, and night had come, the parents opened the room where the boy lay worn out sleeping. They woke him, and gave him wine to drink and dainty things to eat, and they held the feast of his thirteenth birthday.

THE RICH MAN

IN Ropwitz there lived a very wealthy Jew. One day he got into his carriage and rode to Medzibuz to visit Rabbi Israel.

They sat and talked of things that are in this world. But when it was time for the visit to come to an end, the rich man took a purse filled with gold and left it on the Master's table.

Rabbi Israel led the man to the door. There he said, " Is there nothing you wanted to ask of me? "

" No," said the rich man, opening the door. " I only wanted to make a visit. I only wanted to see the rabbi of whom all the world is speaking. And I desired to leave a small present."

The Master looked at the bag of money, and a smile came into his eyes. " And there is nothing I can do to help you? " he asked.

" What help should I need? Gold, the Lord be thanked, I have in great quantity. My children are grown, my daughters are happily married, and my grandchildren are in good health. No, Rabbi, I am not in need of help."

" If you will listen," said the Baal Shem Tov, " I'll tell you a story."

In a city not far from here, almost a hundred years ago, there lived two wealthy Jewish merchants. Their houses stood one next to the other, and as close as their houses were, so were their hearts. Each of these merchants had a son; the boys had been born on the same day, and they grew up together like twin brothers, sharing their lessons and their games and every gift that was given them. When the boys were thirteen years old they swore eternal blood-brotherhood.

The time came for them to be married. The father of one of the boys found a bride for him in a city far to the west, and the young man went there to live. The father of the other boy found a wife for him in a city far to the east, and the young man went there to live. The boys were three hundred miles apart.

In the beginning, they wrote letters every week to each other. But as the ties of their new family lives began to grow around them, and their business affairs absorbed them, they wrote only once each month. And at last they wrote only once a year, and then they did not write at all to each other.

Both of the young men did well in their business, and became very rich.

But after that it happened to one of them that his affairs began to go against him. His ships were lost, his warehouses caught fire, his debtors cheated him, and within a short time he found himself in poverty. Then he remembered his childhood friend.

He took the last coins that were left him, to help him on his way, and he journeyed three hundred miles to the city where his friend lived. He saw that the house of his friend was two stories high, the doors were of black mahogany, the walls were of whitest marble brought from far-distant lands. He entered into the house. The walls were covered with beautiful paintings in golden frames; soft rugs covered the floors, and all manner of costly treasures stood in every room.

The master of the house came running to meet his childhood friend. He fell on his neck for joy, and hugged him to himself, and received him in every way as though he were a brother. " And tell me, how does it go with you? " he said.

Then the traveller answered, " I will tell you the truth. Even the clothes that you see on me, poor as they are, do not belong to me. I am in greatest need."

The rich man called his steward. " Make an account of all my possessions," he said.

When the steward brought him the account, the rich man said, " Divide it into two parts."

Then he gave half of all he possessed to his friend, and kept the other half for himself.

The traveller was overjoyed. He blessed his friend many times. And he took his share of the gold, rode back to his own city, and went into business once more.

This time he prospered. He became the wealthiest man in that city, and for many miles around. In order to hold all of his gold, he had built for himself a house three stories high, and it was built like a strong-house, and surrounded by a fence of pointed irons. The strong-house had no windows, and only one door, which was heavily guarded.

Far up in the farthest corner of this house he built a room of iron, and there he sat day and night, surrounded by his account books and his most precious treasures, occupied with his affairs.

" I have known misery and want," he said. " I shall never be poor again." And every week he became more rich, until he was the richest man in all that land, but still he drove himself to become richer, for fear of being poor.

His friend did not fare so well. From the time he divided his fortune, trouble came into his house. He was robbed by those whom he trusted, he did not have enough gold to meet his undertakings, and soon his house was taken from him, and he became even poorer than the other had been.

For many weeks he suffered starvation. Then he bethought himself of his friend. Joy came over him. " I will go to him! " he said.

He wrote a letter to his friend, saying that he was on his way. " I must come on foot," he said. And he thought, " Surely he will come out on the road to meet me." And he started on foot on the way, begging his food as he went.

Every step of the way he walked with joyous expectation, for at each turning of the road he thought he would find his friend come in a carriage to meet him. But day by day went by, and his journey was almost ended, and still he was not met by his friend.

He thought, " Perhaps he started on another road to find me, and not meeting me returned to his house, where he awaits me."

At last he came to the city, and came before the house of the rich man. He stood before it, and saw how strongly it was built, and saw the iron wall around it. He went to the gate and knocked. The door was not opened to him. But a guard looked through the hole, and saw him, and said, " No beggars are allowed to come into this place."

But the traveller said, " Your master is waiting for me. I am his boyhood friend. Tell him I have come."

The gate-keeper laughed.

However, the ragged traveller hammered so long at the gate, and was so insistent in his plea, that the keeper at last went up to his master, in the iron room in the farthest corner of the house, and said:

"There is a poor beggar at the gate who says he is your boyhood friend. He will not go away, but wishes to speak to you."

Then the rich man thought, "If I allow him to come in to me, and speak with him, my heart will become softened, and I will give him money. Perhaps I will even divide my possessions with him. Then I will fall into poverty once more. For see what has happened to him, who was foolish enough to give away half of his possessions! He has become a beggar! Have I not had enough of poverty in my life? No, I will not risk it!"

And he said to the keeper, "Send him away."

The keeper went to the gate and said to the man, "My master does not know you."

The generous friend cried, "But you do not understand! He does not understand! Tell him it is his brother — !"

All day he cried outside the gate.

He was weak from the long journey, and from hunger, and his heart was broken. He saw that he was about to die.

"I will not die here under his gate," he said. "It will bring dishonour upon him to have a beggar die under his gate." He summoned his last strength, and dragged himself away. Not far from the house of his friend, he fell in the street and died.

A few months passed. The rich man became sick, and also died.

The souls of the two men came together before the Almighty and stood to be judged.

The generous friend was given leave to come into heaven. But the share of the other was hell.

Then the generous friend cried, " I cannot go into heaven without him, for we vowed eternal brotherhood. Let me rather go down to hell with my friend, than remain in heaven alone."

The Almighty said, " Hell is the lot of one, and heaven is the lot of the other. But you, who are doomed to enter heaven, if you do not agree with this judgement, then be yourself the judge, and say what should be done with your two souls."

The generous soul said, " It is not right to condemn my friend only because I died in poverty. Surely there was some mistake when he refused to admit me into his house, perhaps his servant did not make him understand that a beggar asked bread of him. Almighty God, send both our souls back to earth. Let me be born in poverty, and grow up to be a beggar. And let him again be the wealthy man. Let me come to him, and beg for bread."

So it was ordained.

They were born again, one poor, one rich, and they lived in far separate places. And when the poor boy was grown, he was a beggar on the roads.

Once he came to a great city. He came before a costly house. And he thought, " I will go into that house, and ask to see the master, and beg bread of him."

As he went up to the door, a pedlar passed on the street. " Beggar," the pedlar laughed, " spare yourself the trouble of knocking on that door. Everyone knows that the master of that house has never given away so much as a crumb of bread to a bird."

Yet the beggar knocked.

He came into a great empty room. He saw the master of the house standing in the middle of the room. He went up to him and said, " I am starving. Give me a crust of bread."

The man looked at the beggar, and laughed out loud. " Every child in the street knows that I never give alms," he said. " You are foolish to come here to beg."

But the wanderer, though he did not know who he was himself, or who the rich man was, began to beg with all the passion of his soul, as though his life, here and hereafter, depended on a crust of bread from the hand of this rich man, and from no other.

He fell on his knees, and his eyes were wild as with fever. " Do not send me from you empty-handed! " he cried. " Do not let me starve! "

The rich man became angry. He shouted at the beggar, " Go away! " But the beggar would not go. Then the rich man seized him by his shoulders and lifted him to his feet. Their faces came close to each other, and for an instant they saw into each other's eyes.

" Give! " cried the beggar, with his last breath.

The rich man slapped his hand across the beggar's mouth.

The beggar was already weakened by hunger, and strained by the wild passion that had taken possession of him. The cord of his life was ragged, and hung on a single thread. And the blow snapped that thread in two. The beggar fell down lifeless.

The Baal Shem Tov stopped talking, for he had finished telling the story.

Then he looked at his visitor and said, " And have you still nothing to ask of me? "

The wealthy man could hardly breathe. " I am that wealthy man! " he gasped. " Rabbi, what shall I do? "

" Take all that you possess," said Rabbi Israel, " and sell it for gold. Take all the gold with you, and go along the road. Whenever you meet a poor man, or a needy one, say to yourself that he is of your dead friend's family. Give away all the gold that you possess to the great family of poor people that your friend has left in this world, and when you have given away all that you possess, beg, and give what is given you to those more needy than yourself. Give, and love those to whom you are giving."

The rich man listened to the words of Rabbi Israel. Then he went out, and left his carriage, and began walking along the road.

THE TRIAL OF RABBI GERSHON

RABBI GERSHON of Kuth would not believe in the power of his brother-in-law. He said, " Rabbi Israel is nothing but a lime-burner come out of the mountains. He couldn't even earn a living as a tavern-keeper."

Once he went to Medzibuz to visit his sister. And he thought, " Let me see the wonder-working of this brother-in-law of mine." So he remained over the Sabbath.

On Friday afternoon, he saw Rabbi Israel prepare for the mincha prayer. " But it is still very early," said Rabbi Gershon. Nevertheless, the Master began to pray. And when Rabbi Israel came to say the bene-dictions, he remained standing motionless on his feet for four whole hours. Perspiration was upon his fore-head, and his face was in an agony of labour. But at last he made an end to his prayer.

" Why did you take four hours to say the benedic-tions? " asked Rabbi Gershon.

" Stay until next Sabbath," said Rabbi Israel, " and I shall teach you how to say the benedictions as I say them."

Now, the truth was that when the Master said the benedictions on the eve of Sabbath, he first uttered the Word of the Will, that sundered the bonds of all dead and living souls. Then myriads of dead souls came rushing toward him out of their eternal wander-ing in nothingness, and begged him to put them in his prayers, so that his prayers might at last carry them into heaven.

When he uttered the words " Quicken the dead! " he was always surrounded by these innumerable exiled souls, and it was the labour of carrying these souls into heaven that occupied him for so many hours. But at this labour he worked unceasingly, lifting the dead souls onto the wings of his powerful prayers, and sending them into heaven, until he heard the Daughter of the Voice call " Holy! Holy! " Then he knew that no more souls could be admitted into heaven on that day, and he made an end to his prayer.

On the following Friday afternoon, the Baal Shem Tov said to his brother-in-law Rabbi Gershon, " I will tell you a word to utter before you begin the mincha prayer. Then you will understand why I remain so many hours over the benedictions." And he whispered the secret Word of the Will to Rabbi Gershon.

Rabbi Gershon repeated the Word, and began to say mincha.

But Rabbi Israel himself did not begin to pray. He stood and toyed with his tobacco pouch, and fingered the alms-box, and waited. He waited until Rabbi Gershon came to the words " Quicken the dead! "

And in that instant there came a terrible rush of souls, thousands upon thousands of dead souls came flying, to crowd weeping and shrieking and begging around the praying Rabbi Gershon. And Rabbi Gershon fainted with fright.

When the Baal Shem Tov had taken care of his brother-in-law, he set himself to say the benedictions, and helped those thousands of souls into heaven.

Rabbi Gershon wanted to become greater than his brother-in-law.

In Eretz Israel, at that time, there lived the celebrated Rabbi Chayim ben Atar, who was known as Ohr Ha-Chayim, which means the Living Light.

There is a power that is even beyond the power of the Word. And that furthest power consists of Two that are One. It is the power of chaos and creation, it is the power of eternity within the instant.

And half of that power was in the Ohr Ha-Chayim, while the other half of that power was in the Baal Shem Tov. The soul of Rabbi Chayim ben Atar was the complement of the soul of Rabbi Israel ben Eleazer. The soul of Rabbi Israel was affirmation, and the soul of Rabbi Chayim was negation. If these two souls would be united, the beginning and the end would become One.

Rabbi Gershon went to Eretz Yisroael, to become the disciple of the Ohr Ha-Chayim.

Rabbi Gershon spoke to the Ohr Ha-Chayim of his brother-in-law. He said, " My brother-in-law Rabbi Israel believes he walks in heaven."

The Ohr Ha-Chayim knew of the power of Rabbi Israel. For in their goings up to heaven, both of them had sat in the highest regions where Rabbi Hillel propounds the Torah to the elect of all souls. And the Ohr Ha-Chayim, who was the end, knew of the fate of Rabbi Israel.

The Ohr Ha-Chayim said to Rabbi Gershon, " Ask of your brother-in-law whether he can see every part of himself when he walks in heaven."

Rabbi Gershon thought: " See how the Ohr Ha-Chayim makes fun of my brother-in-law! " And he

wrote in a letter to Rabbi Israel: " The Ohr Ha-
Chayim asks whether you can see yourself from head
to foot when you walk in heaven."

But this letter was long in reaching the Baal Shem
Tov.

RABBI ISRAEL'S DAUGHTER

THE Baal Shem's daughter Udel was a grown girl. She said to him, " Father, when shall I know my husband? " Rabbi Israel loved his daughter; he stroked her hair. She said, " Father, shall I be a mother of children? "

Rabbi Israel told her, " Your husband is hidden among the scholars who come here to me. You must wait until a sign points him out to you."

On Simchas Torah, the feast of the Law, there was joyous dancing in the house of the Baal Shem Tov. The students danced, and Israel danced with them, they danced with wildest ecstasy for love of the holy Torah. And in the midst of their mad whirling, one of the students lost his shoe. It flew right off his foot.

Then he sang out a popular verse:

> " A maiden will put
> The shoe on my foot,
> A mother will rock
> The babe in her cradle! "

Just then Rabbi Israel cried to his daughter, " Udel!"

Then the girl became so confused she didn't know where to find the student's slipper. So she sat down and took off both of her own slippers and gave them to the young man.

And she married that man. And from their union two sons and a daughter were born. One son grew up to be the Tsadik of Sadilikov, and the other was Rabbi Baruch of Medzibuz. The daughter was named Feige.

PRAYER

ONCE Rabbi Israel passed through a house of prayer. An old Jew sat there huddled over a book, reading in a hasty mumble, reading faster and faster, hour after hour.

Rabbi Israel said, " He is so absorbed in his learning that he has forgotten there is a God over the world."

THRICE HE LAUGHED

THE MYSTERIOUS LAUGHTER OF THE BAAL SHEM
TOV, AND THE SABBATH OF SABBATAI,
THE BOOK-BINDER

THE meal of Sabbath eve was ready upon the
table.

Rabbi Israel's head was sunken, and anxiety was
deep upon his face. His scholars, seated about the long
table, were silent.

The Baal Shem arose and began to speak the blessing over the wine. He lifted his glass.

And all at once a golden shine of joy spread over his
cheeks and eyes; he raised his glass, threw back his
head, and broke forth in merry laughter. He laughed
until he had to wipe bright tears from his eyes.

The scholars could not understand what might
have caused the Rabbi's laughter. They looked one
to another, they looked at the Rabbi, they looked
all about the room. But everything was as always.
The candles burned, casting their shine upon the
long white tablecloth, and upon the plates that bore
the Sabbath meal, and upon the cups of Sabbath
wine.

The Master had ceased laughing. But all the sadness was gone from his face. He drank his wine, and
sat cheerily to his meal.

He began to eat of the fish. Suddenly he set down
his hand. His eyes looked far away. And again he
broke out into laughter.

During the entire Sabbath, it was the custom of the
scholars never to ask questions of the Baal Shem Tov.
Therefore they could not ask him the cause of his

strange and sudden joy. They ate, and looked one to the other, and wondered.

And when Rabbi Israel was eating soup, he broke out for the third time into laughter. And this time he laughed with the easy contentment of a father watching his children at play.

That night, and all through the Sabbath, the students gathered in groups and discussed the Rabbi's laughter. Three times he had laughed. And they sought in the Torah for explanation of his joy. But they could find no certain answer.

It was the custom of Rabbi Israel in the evening after the out-going of Sabbath to receive one of the scholars into his cabin, and to answer any question that might have arisen among the disciples during the day of rest.

As evening came, the scholars all gathered together, and chose Rabbi Wolf from among themselves to go to the Master and ask why he had broken out three times into laughter during the Sabbath meal.

Rabbi Wolf went to the hut in the forest, to which the Baal Shem Tov often withdrew for solitary contemplation. Rabbi Wolf knocked, and entered.

Rabbi Israel asked, smiling, " What questions have the scholars today? "

" They would like to know," said Rabbi Wolf, " why the Master laughed three times during the meal on the eve of Sabbath."

" Come," said the Baal Shem Tov, " we will get into the wagon and ride, and perhaps you will find out the answer to your question."

Often, on the evening after Sabbath, Rabbi Israel and his students would get into his wagon, and ride on the country roads.

Now they harnessed the horses, and all of the scholars got into the wagon, and all were silent.

The night was soft, it was pleasant. The Baal Shem left the reins lying loosely over his knees. The horses ambled down a forgotten lane. And the Baal Shem hummed to himself, and soon all of the chassidim were humming.

So they rode hour after hour, and instead of turning back they rode onward, and they rode all through the night.

On Sunday morning they found themselves in a village which they had never before seen. Rabbi Israel halted the wagon in front of a tiny synagogue; he got down, and called the shamash.

Soon it was known among all the Jews in the village that the great Rabbi Israel, the Baal Shem Tov, was come among them. Men and women hastened to the market-place, and mothers ran carrying their children to the Rabbi for his blessing, while childless women sought the touch of his hand.

When a great many people had assembled, he said, " Are all the Jews of the village here? "

The head of the congregation looked from one to the other and said, " All."

But Rabbi Israel looked among them as though he sought for someone; and at last he said, " Where is Sabbatai, the book-binder? "

The shamash ran at once to call the aged Sabbatai. In a moment the shamash returned, followed by a small, grey-haired man, whose blue eyes shone clearly in a mild face.

" Let his wife also be called," said Rabbi Israel.

Then Sabbatai hurried and fetched his wife.

When the two of them were there, Rabbi Israel

asked them to stand in the centre of the market-place. On one side of them were all the Jews of the town. And on the other side were Rabbi Israel's scholars.

" Now," said the Master, " tell me, Sabbatai, exactly what you did on last Sabbath eve! But tell me everything, and do not be ashamed, or afraid to speak! "

" Master," said Sabbatai, " I shall indeed tell you everything that happened to me, and what I did; and if it is God's will that I be punished, I am ready to accept his punishment, asking no more than to serve Him."

Then the aged book-binder told his story:

You must know that since my youth I have lived in this village and practised my craft as a book-binder. In those early years, when I was filled with vigour, I was able to manage a thriving business, and I lived on all that was best in the world.

My little wife and I loved to dress well and to have good things to eat, and this we permitted ourselves, for as long as I had enough work to do there was no lack of money. Perhaps we were even somewhat extravagant in buying costly clothing, but my wife was the prettiest girl in the village, and I wanted to see her clothed as became her beauty. And when we drove to the neighbouring villages, I too had to be dressed in a way that would not put her to shame.

So it happened that we spent all the money that I earned, never putting away anything for later years.

With all that, we led honest and observant lives. From my earliest youth it was the custom in our house to strictly observe the Sabbath. On Thursday afternoon my wife would go to the market and buy fish, meat, flour, candles, and all things that were needed for the Sabbath. On Friday morning at ten o'clock I would put aside my work, close my shop, and go to the synagogue. There I would remain until night fell, when I would go home to the Sabbath meal. Coming toward the house, I would see the lighted candles shining through the window, and I would know that everything was well in my house.

But during these last years, the weakness of old age has come upon me. I have no sons to help me. And it seems that, little by little, the world is forgetting me. I no longer receive much work from the neighbouring villages. And as I am not as vigorous as I was in my youth, I cannot go out to seek more work. Therefore it goes hard with me these years.

There have been days when we did not have a penny for buying bread. On those days, we fasted. For I said to my wife, " The people among whom we live are kind-hearted and charitable, and they would be generous toward us if they knew of our plight. But I have lived all my life without asking help of anyone but God, and so I would finish my days."

Last Thursday, when my wife was ready to go out to the market, she saw that there was no money in the house, and no food, not even a bit of flour-dust to bake into bread. She came to me and asked me what money I had, but I had earned nothing at all that day. " Perhaps by tomorrow morning," I said, " some work will come into the shop." Then she went home, and for the first time during our years of marriage, my wife did not do her Sabbath marketing on Thursday afternoon.

On Friday morning no work came. Then I said to

my wife, " Let us fast throughout this Sabbath. But above all we must not let our neighbours know that we are in need. For the neighbouring women would come with meat, and fish, and Sabbath-bread, and you would not be able to refuse their offerings."

Then I made a plan, and said to my wife, " I will tell you how we must manage. I will remain late in the synagogue, later than usual. I will stay until all the others have gone. Then I will be able to come home without meeting anyone who may ask me: Sabbatai, why are there no candles lit in your house? I would not know how to answer such a question. And when I come home at night, we will praise God, accepting what he has given us."

So my good wife agreed. And at ten o'clock in the morning I closed the door of my shop, and went to the synagogue.

In our little house my wife sat, and as there was no Sabbath meal to prepare, she had nothing to do. As she did not like to sit empty-handed, she began to clean the house again. She cleaned the bare table and washed the empty pots, she brushed the vacant cupboard, she swept and dusted where there was no particle of dust, and when she was finished the house was perfect as a jewel.

Still time went long with her. Then she began to seek for other things to do. And she bethought herself of the great chest filled with old clothing. " I will put the old clothing in order," she said, " and clean it, and mend what needs to be mended."

In the chest were all the fine clothes we had worn in our youth. And there among the garments she found a coat that I had worn when we went to the villages to dance, and on that coat were seven buttons covered with gold. My wife was overjoyed! She took her scissors and cut the golden buttons from the coat. She ran with them to the goldsmith. He weighed the gold, and paid her the worth of it in money. Then she hastened to the market. She bought meat, and fish, and flour, and fine tall candles, and she had enough money to buy wine for the Sabbath blessing, and to buy all the other necessities for a perfect Sabbath! Then she went home, and all during the afternoon she was busy preparing the Sabbath meal.

When darkness came, and all the others had gone from the synagogue, I walked slowly toward my house. I met no one on the way, and for that at least I was glad, as I thought I would not have known what to answer if someone had met and asked me, " Sabbatai, why are there no candles in your house tonight? "

But as I came near the house, I saw the light of candles! Then I thought, my good wife has not been able to withstand this trial, and has taken the help of neighbours.

I came into the house. I saw the white cloth spread on the table, and upon the cloth was arranged a beautiful Sabbath meal. I saw fish and meat and fresh-baked Sabbath bread, and soup, and wine for the blessing.

Then, as I did not want to break the peace and joy of the Sabbath, I said nothing to my wife. I withheld the disappointment that I felt when I thought that she had accepted gifts from our neighbours. I spoke the blessing over the wine, and over the meal, and I sat down to the Sabbath table.

But after a while I spoke to her as gently as I might,

so that she would not feel hurt at my words. I said, " My good wife, I see that you were not able to refuse the kindness of our neighbours, for you are a soft-hearted woman."

But she smiled in a strange joyous way, and laughed at me, and said, " My honest Sabbatai, do you remember the costly coat you had when you were young, your coat with the golden buttons? Today, having nothing with which to occupy my hands, I searched in the old clothes-chest, and I found your coat. I cut off the buttons and took them to the goldsmith, and he gave me money with which I bought all that we needed for the Sabbath, and there is enough money left for food for another day! "

Master! My heart was so filled with joy that I could not contain myself. Tears went from my eyes. Once more I praised the Lord for not having forgotten his children. And I praised him again and again, happy that it was from God himself, and not from man, that we had received our Sabbath.

My heart was filled with singing. I forgot the majesty of the Sabbath. And I took my wife by the hands, and led her out, and we danced in our little house. Then we sat down to eat. But when she served the fish course, I was so overcome with joy that I took her in my arms and danced with her again. And when we ate our soup, we danced a third time, and laughed and cried for happiness. For my soul overflowed with the glory of God, and I could not shut my heart over the terrible joy that was in it.

But, Master, it came to me afterward that perhaps our dancing and laughter had disturbed the sublimity of God's Sabbath; and if we have sinned in such a

SABBATH MEAL

way, and you have come here to find us out, then speak a full punishment over me and my wife, and we will accept it, and do all that remains in our power to fulfil the punishment that you put upon us, and come once more into the grace of God.

So spoke the book-binder, Sabbatai, while his wife stood by his side.

Then Rabbi Israel said to his scholars, and to all who were assembled there, " Know, that all the hierarchy of Heaven sang, and laughed, and was joyful, and danced hand in hand with this aged man and his wife when they were happy on Sabbath eve. And there was a golden joy spread all through Paradise, and joy filled the Eternal Heart. And for the three times you heard my laughter, my friends, I was here with them when they went out three times to dance, and I danced, and I sang with them! "

THE BURNING OF THE TORAH

HERE IS THE TALE OF THE TERRIFIC STRUGGLE BETWEEN
THE BAAL SHEM TOV AND THE ENEMY, WHO
BY FOUL TRICKERY SOUGHT TO HAVE THE
TORAH TAKEN AWAY FROM THE JEWS

THEN the Enemy, tormented as he saw Rabbi Israel doing good on earth, schemed to overcome the Master. He called all the angels of darkness into conclave about him and said, " This is my plan:

" I will station dark angels on all the roads that lead to heaven. And whenever and wherever a prayer rises seeking to go upward and enter the Gates of heaven, the dark angels will seize it and throttle it and prevent it from reaching the Gates. Those prayers that have already wandered many years in limbo, they as well as the new prayers shall be prevented from arriving. And thus, no prayers will come before the Throne.

" When many days shall have passed with not a single prayer attaining the Throne, I will go up to God and say to him, ' Look, how your people have deserted you. They no longer send prayers up to you. Even your favourite among the puppets, your devoted Rabbi Israel, has ceased to worship you. Take back your wisdom from Rabbi Israel, and deprive his people of your Torah! ' "

This was the plan of Satan.

At once his ministers of evil crept out upon all the roads that led to heaven. No turning-point, no by-path was left unguarded. Silent, and invisible, they lay in wait. Before the Gates of heaven, a great army of them were in ambush. No prayer could pass.

As the prayers came upward, the angels seized them from behind, and leaped upon them, and throttled them. They could not kill the prayers, but flung them sidewards into chaos. All space was filled with the whimpering and moaning of wounded prayers that stumbled in search of their way.

But every Friday, the prayers came forward in such swarms that all the angels of evil were not numerous enough to stop them. Then many prayers escaped along the roads, and made their way to the Gates of heaven. But here, the army that lay in wait before the Gates of heaven stopped them, and did not allow them to enter.

Thus, weeks went by, and no prayers came up to the Throne.

Then Satan went to God and said, " Take away the Torah from the Jews."

God said, " Give them until the Day of Atonement."

But Satan was impatient. " Send out the command at once! " he said. " Though it be not done until the Day of Atonement."

God gave the terrible command.

Then, on earth, the Archbishop issued a proclamation to all his bishops. " In ten days' time," he said, " seize all of the Hebrew books of learning. Go among the Jews and take their Torah out of their synagogues and out of their houses. Heap the books into pyres, and burn them."

The Bishop of Kamenitz-Podolsky was the most zealous to follow the commands of the Archbishop. He sent his servants into all the houses of the Jews. The Bishop of Lemberg was also zealous. And all

of the bishops did as they had been commanded
to do.

The tenth day would be the Day of Atonement.
And on that day, in a thousand pyres lighted in every
corner of the land, the Torah would burn.

When the Torah began to be taken from the Jews,
the Baal Shem knew that Satan had done a terrible
work. Yet he could not find out what strange evil the
Enemy had done, and he did not know how to
battle against him.

Each day, the suffering and the horror among the
Jews became greater. As the Torah was wrenched
from their arms, they wept and beat themselves as
mothers whose babes are torn from their breasts. And
they said, " On the Day of Atonement we will go into
the flames with our Torah! "

Fasting, and sleepless, night and day the Baal Shem
strove for his people. Day and night he sent mighty
prayers heavenward, they rose colossal on powerful
wings and shot upward with incredible speed. But
the Enemy was on guard every instant in every
crevice of the heavens, the Enemy himself caught the
prayers of the Baal Shem, and threw them from their
way.

The heart of the Baal Shem was become a gusty cave
of grief.

At last came the Day of Atonement.

Rabbi Israel went into the synagogue to hold the
prayer service. At his side stood Rabbi Yacob.

And all those who were in the synagogue saw the
terrible fever of struggle that lay over the face of the
Baal Shem Tov. Hope came into their bleak hearts.
" He will save us today," they said.

When the moment came for the utterance of Kol Nidro, Rabbi Israel lifted his voice, his voice sang through the shreds of his torn heart; all who listened were frozen with sorrow.

In the service of the lamentations it was the custom for Rabbi Yacob to read each verse aloud, then Rabbi Israel would repeat the verse after him. And so they began the lamentations.

But when Rabbi Yacob read out the verse, " Open the Portals of Heaven! " there was no sound from Rabbi Israel. Rabbi Yacob waited. The synagogue quaked in a terrific silence. And Rabbi Israel remained silent. Rabbi Yacob repeated, " Open the Portals of Heaven! " But still the Master did not utter a word.

Then, in that fever of silence, Rabbi Israel threw himself upon the ground, and beat his head against the ground, and out of him there came a cry that was like the roar of a dying lion.

Rabbi Israel remained doubled upon the ground. His body quivered with the might of the struggle. For two hours he remained with his head bent upon the ground.

And those who were in the house of prayer could not take their eyes from him; they did not dare to approach him, but watched him, and were silent.

At last Rabbi Israel raised himself. His face was a face of wonders.

He said, " The Portals of Heaven are open! "

And thus he ended the service.

Long afterward, what he had done during the two hours when he lay with his head to the ground became known.

He had gone up to the Palace of the Eternal. He had gone up to the greatest of Gates, that stands over the road that leads directly to the Throne. There, huddled before the Gate, he had found hundreds and thousands of prayers. Some of them were maimed, some lay gasping as though they had just ended a terrible struggle, some were emaciated and old, some were blind through wandering in darkness.

" What are you waiting for! " asked the Baal Shem. " Why don't you go in, and approach the Throne of the Almighty? "

They said, " Until this moment, the angels of darkness were on guard, and would not let us approach the Gate. But as they saw you coming, they fled. Now we are waiting for your prayer, to take us within the Portals."

" I will take you in," said the Baal Shem Tov.

But just at the moment when he sought to pass through the Gate, the army of Evil ones who had rushed behind the Gate when they saw his approach pushed the Gate forward, and closed it. Then the Enemy himself came out. In his two hands he carried a lock. He hung the lock upon the great Portal.

The Gate is as big as the world. And the lock was as big as a city.

The Baal Shem went up to the lock and walked around it, seeking some crack through which he might enter, and through which he might lead the prayers. But the lock was of solid iron, and there was no crack anywhere.

The road to the throne was closed.

But the Baal Shem did not despair.

It is known that for each of us on earth there lives

a being in heaven. And that being is exactly as we are.

Into that nether region of heaven the way was open. Then Rabbi Israel went in there, and sought out his counterpart, who was the Rabbi Israel of heaven.

And Rabbi Israel of the earth said to him, " What shall I do, to bring the prayers before the Name? "

Rabbi Israel of heaven said, " There is only one thing to do. Let us go to the palace of Messiah."

They came to the palace where Messiah sits awaiting the day when he may go down to earth.

And as soon as the Baal Shem entered, Messiah cried out to him, " Be joyous! I will help you! " And he gave the Baal Shem a token.

The Baal Shem took the token, and went back to the Gate that was locked. Before the token, the lock fell away, and the Portals opened wide as the earth is large, and all the prayers entered and went straight to the Throne of the Name.

Then there was joy all through the heavens, and the good angels sang paeans of joy, while the dark angels crept and slunk away to the farthest corners of chaos.

In that moment, the Bishop of Kamenitz-Podolsky kindled a fire on earth. He stood by the fire that he had kindled. At his side was a great pile of volumes of Hebrew writings, hundreds of tractates of the Talmud were there in that pyramid.

The Bishop of Kamenitz-Podolsky took a tractate of the Talmud, and hurled it into the fire. It began to burn. The Bishop took another book, and hurled it into the flames. They rose higher, they leaped mightily upward. Again and again the Bishop hurled the Talmud into the flames. But when he had thrown seven tractates into the flames, and was about to throw the eighth, his hand was seized with a trembling, and then his whole body was seized with shaking, and he fell in an epileptic fit.

All the multitude shivered with terror, and ran from the burning-place. The fire died down, and went out.

And the news of this spread swiftly, as a pestilence on the wind. Then all those bishops who had builded pyres of holy books, and prepared to burn them, were frightened, fearing that the curse of the Baal Shem would come upon them, and they would be seized with horrible spasms. They left the books in their market-places, and ran into their towers for safety.

Thus the Talmud was saved for the Jews on the Day of Atonement.

THE BOY'S SONG

THE Enemy did not forswear the battle, but came out openly and spread his iron wings between the earth and heaven. The wings were as thick as a mountain is high, and all through they were made of heavy iron. He wrapped his wings around the earth as he would enclose it within the two cups of his hand.

On earth, all was darkness. The wings of the Enemy pressed forever closer to the earth, and crushed the spirits of men.

When Rabbi Israel was about to enter into a synagogue, he stopped outside the door and said, " I cannot go in there. There is no room for me to enter."

But the chassidim said, " There are not many people in the synagogue."

" The house is filled from the ground to the roof with prayers! " said the Master.

But as he saw the chassidim taking pride because of his words, he said, "Those prayers are all dead prayers. They have no strength to fly to heaven. They are crushed, they lie one on top of the other, the house is filled with them."

And he returned to Medzibuz.

He felt the weight of the wings of the Enemy pressing ever closer upon him. He sought for a way to pierce that iron cloud, and make a path to Heaven.

Not far from Medzibuz there lived a Jewish herdsman. This man had an only son, the boy was twelve years old but so slow-witted that he could not remember the alphabet. For several years the Jew had sent his son to the cheder, but as the boy could not remember anything, the father ceased to send him to the school, and instead sent him into the fields to mind the cows.

The boy took a reed and made himself a flute, and sat all day long in the grass, playing upon his flute.

But when the boy reached his thirteenth birthday, his father said, " After all, he must be taught some shred of Jewishness." So he said to the lad, " Come, we will go to the synagogue for the holidays."

He got in his wagon, and drove his son to Medzibuz, and bought him a cap and new shoes. And all that time, David carried his flute in his pocket.

His father took him to the synagogue of Rabbi Israel.

They sat together among the other men. The boy was very still.

Then the moment came for the prayer of mussaf to be said. David saw the men all about him raise their little books, and read out of them in praying, singing voices. He saw his father do as the other men did. Then David pulled at his father's arm.

" Father," he said, " I too want to sing. I have my flute in my pocket. I'll take it out, and sing."

But his father caught his hand. " Be still! " he whispered. " Do you want to make the Rabbi angry? Be still! "

David sat quietly on the bench.

Until the prayer of mincha, he did not move. But

when the men arose to repeat the mincha prayer, the boy also arose. "Father," he said, "I too want to sing!"

His father whispered quickly, "Where have you got your fife?"

"Here in my pocket."

"Let me see it."

David drew out his fife, and showed it to his father. His father seized it out of his hand. "Let me hold it for you," he said.

David wanted to cry, but was afraid, and remained still.

At last came the prayer of neilah. The candles burned trembling in the evening wind, and the hearts of the worshippers trembled as the flames of the candles. All through the house was the warmth of holiness, and the stillness as before the Presence. Then the outspread palms of the Rabbi were raised over them, and the words of the eighteen benedictions were spoken.

The boy could hold back his desire no longer. He seized the flute from his father's hand, set it to his mouth, and began to play his music.

A silence of terror fell upon the congregation. Aghast, they looked upon the boy; their backs cringed, as if they waited instantly for the walls to fall upon them.

But a flood of joy came over the countenance of Rabbi Israel. He raised his spread palms over the boy David.

"The cloud is pierced and broken!" cried the Master of the Name, "and evil is scattered from over the face of the earth!"

THE WANDERING IN HEAVEN

DURING the day, the Master served all living creatures. From far away they came, begging Life of him; supplicating voices flowed from the mouths of all breathing beings, and the breath of their suffering reached toward him.

He took of his Power, and divided it among them. Unendingly he gave his strength out of himself. Unendingly his Faith flowed to them, in answer.

Under the touch of his finger the wounds of the world were healed.

During the day, he served all living creatures. But at night his soul took freedom. She would no longer remain among the suffering. She shook off time and space as two imprisoning fetters, and raised herself to the borders. She shook off the earth from her foot. She tried her wings. And the Heavens received her.

In Heaven, there is neither time nor space, but infinity and eternity. Each night the soul went further into infinity, deeper into eternity. She followed the living path.

But there came one night when a wall of earth stood before the soul, barring her way. Boundless as had been her flight, so was the barrier boundless. The living path came against the wall, and died. A dark finger had put out all the light of all the stars and covered the warmth of all heaven.

And the wall had a countenance, formless and shadowy, yet it seemed to the soul to be more familiar than her own self. And the soul recognized it, for it was the face of the human life that she had left in the evening, and to which she had to return in the morning, as into a warmed bed.

But from the other side of the wall there wakened a sound, a great voice in the darkness. It was as though the Path lived again on the other side of the wall, and wakened and spoke:

The Voice of the Unknown spoke:

" Soul, yearning soul, soul of power and of dreams. Soul that seeks for all things, space and infinity, object and mystery at once! This is the boundary. Here is the altar of the world. Beyond this boundary, human life may not pass, for the name of this place is God's Wall.

" Unto this spot reaches variety. Beyond this spot, the Oneness begins.

" Soul that has come unto this silent, impenetrable wall —

" Sever yourself from earthly life, and I will open to you. Or return in your flight. For whoever has passed beyond me, does not return."

And the Voice sank. And again there was nothing before the soul but the dim, silent wall.

The soul lifted her head. For the space of an instant she stood, as though listening to the resounding word, and then she spoke her answer:

" I depart from the — "

In that instant, on earth, a woman leaned over a bed in which lay the body of a man. She looked, she touched the pale deathlike sleeper. Then she cried, " Israel! "

Her cry flew straight to Heaven. Her cry was swifter than the spirit of the stars, swifter than the angel of death. Before that instant was closed, the cry stood at the end of the Path upon which the soul had passed so many nights, and the cry put his hand over her shoulder.

Then the soul withheld her words, and looked behind herself. And she spoke no more. She put her arm about the neck of the messenger, and returned in her flight.

That was the last time the Master wandered toward Heaven.

THE PROPHECY OF THE NEW YEAR

LITTLE by little Rabbi Israel had given Power out of himself, that the weaker might be sustained. The well of his Force was deep, and might never become dry, yet the Power was not in him now as in earlier years. His soul went no more into Heaven, and yet he yearned for Heaven.

Then he desired to bring down Heaven on earth.

Though he knew the time had not yet come, he could not restrain his desire, and all of the strength that remained in him gathered and mounted for that attempt.

The pale first sun of the new year hung far in the midst of grey heaven, and the air was filled with the sound of the ram's horn blown in trumpet call. Some thought they could even see the sounds of the trumpet spreading in a faint glowing orbit through the greyness of the autumn day, as the call went forward.

The students sat about the long ancient table in the house of the Baal Shem Tov. Today it seemed to root its gnarled feet into the very ground, and take a new hold on life. Some of the students looked out into the halo of spreading light, and some sat staring at the blackened walls, as though the next instant the walls must draw aside and reveal the Empire of Mystery.

The prayer was ended. The Master began to speak the sermon of the New Year.

The students had not the strength to look into his

glowing face; but when they closed their eyes each of his words came before them, and each word had a form; some were ablaze in light, some shadow dark, and some were pure and stainless as God's love on earth. With their eyes closed they sat, young and aged, and listened, and saw.

The voice of Rabbi Israel was ever as a gently sounded bell, though when he uttered fullest prayer his voice became as the cry of the lark's throat. But on the day of the New Year his voice was fresh and nimble. The ram's horn breathed through him and became a human call. The song of the *Tekia* knocked on the door of the soul, calling " come away "! The wavering notes of the *Scherwarim* wakened the freed souls like the freshness of day, and filled them with the tremblement of eternal longing. The high joyous cry of the *Terua* carried them up to Redemption.

And the Word upon which the Baal Shem spoke was the Word of the New Year:

" Sound on the mighty trumpet the sound of our Release! "

" Sound on the mighty trumpet! " he cried to the Almighty. " When the sphere of the year is rounded, and the souls of all things reach through the darkness toward a new birth, sound! See, Your children are become bitten under the assault of the storm. See, the fire of the wilderness has left her mark on them. But now the circle of Your year closes. The awful darkness on the other side has sent out her chill waves before her, already we feel their approach. Sound on the mighty Trumpet, O Lord, for the new Birth!

" Your punishment has bitten into our hand and

eaten out the strength of life. Your banishment has hounded our feet until they tottered on solid earth. You sent the worm into our hearts, and they are gnawed like withered leaves. We have felt the icy hand of Your Will upon our foreheads, and our thoughts are stiffened and glazed. Sound on the mighty trumpet, O Lord, for our Release!

" The Angel of the Lord took hold of me during the night and led me outward, and I stood in nothingness, and the night lay upon my shoulders like a great burden, and the night rolled from below my prisoned feet. Then the Angel said, See! and the darkness faded, and I stood in a whited nothingness, and I saw.

" There between two chasms stood a narrow circular ridge. And within the ridge was enclosed a red depth like a sea of blood, and outside of it was a black depth like a sea of Night. And I saw, there walked a man upon the ridge, he walked like a blind man, with trembling feet, and his two weak arms wavered feeling against the darkness on one side of him and on the other; and his breast was all of glass, and I saw his heart flutter like a sick leaf in the wind, and on his brow was the mark of the icy Hand. The man went further and further around the ridge, without seeing to right or to left, and he was nearly come to the end of the circle, where his beginning had been. And I wanted to call to him, but that which I saw stopped my tongue, and I could not move it, as though it were stone. For suddenly the man had raised his eyes and seen what was on the right and on the left of him, then he staggered, and from each chasm arms reached upward to seize him.

" Then the Angel touched my lips, and my tongue

was free, and I called and I shouted to him, " Lift up your wings and fly! " Then behold, the man lifted up wings! there was no more weakness or fear in him; then the ridge faded from beneath his feet, and the chasm of blood was dissolved in God's spring-water, and the chasm of night melted in God's light, and the City of the Lord lay before me, open everyways.

" Behold, the year is a circle. We go on a narrow circular ridge between two chasms, and we do not see their depth. But when we come to the end of the way that is also its beginning, then the trembling of fear falls upon us as before the thunder from on high, and the lightning of the Lord flashes over the chasm, and we see the chasm, and we quiver.

" Then the trumpet sounds over us, and takes hold of our souls and carries them, each call of the trumpet carries myriads of souls upon its wings! And the sounds of the trumpet leap up to Heaven, and the Heavens listen, and fear and trembling comes over the Heavens as before the thunder of the Lord; and the trumpet resounds! And the Trumpet of the World carries on its wings that soul that shall be born out of all our souls, and is the soul of Messiah. And he climbs up to the Kingdom of Mysteries, and he beats with his wings on the Door, and the Door falls open, and behold, there is neither door nor wall remaining, but the City of God lies there, open everyways.

" Sound on the mighty trumpet, O Lord, for the birth of the Soul! "

The voice of the Baal Shem Tov was like the trumpet, until it ceased. Then he arose from the table, and went into his chamber, and locked himself there. And there he remained, motionless in striving. For his utmost power was gone forward in his demand, and his soul awaited surely the coming of Messiah.

And the students also arose from about the table, and went out. As sleepwalkers they went through the streets, unseeing, and filled with yearning. At the borders of the city there was a hut where they would come together that they might undisturbed occupy themselves with thoughts of the Eternal. There they now went. And the Wings of the Voice were still over them.

But at that time there lived in the house of the Baal Shem Tov a young boy whose name was Joseph, and who was called Yohseleh. When the Master had gone into his chamber, and the students had all gone to their cottage outside the city, the boy remained alone at the long table, for he was too young to go with the others to their meditations. Yohseleh remained sitting there, within the darkening walls, and he felt the wings of the Voice upon his shoulders.

And when the first shadow of the twilight trembled goldenbrown over the white table-cloth, Yohseleh laid his head on his hands, he was in terror before the Will of the Voice, and he sank under the heaviness of the wings of the Voice that were on his shoulders. His closed fingers, pressed before his eyes, set him into deepest darkness; but in that darkness there wakened a Light that sang with the same Voice whose will he so feared. The Voice pressed upon Yohseleh with an irresistible force, and like tears long held

back it suddenly burst forth, and Yohseleh cried,
" Now and at once Messiah must come! "

Then the room became as far away, and the walls
disappeared, and before him was a Light that gave
out rings of illumination, as a night-time sun. And
Yoseleh ran toward the Light. But here was the door,
like a piercing, wakening pain. The boy stood for a
second, as one on a narrow ridge between two chasms,
who suddenly sees his danger. The Lightning of the
Lord went out of him, and he was afraid, shuddering.
But then the Power seized him as with the strength
of the Cherubim, and the Voice cried, and Light fell
once more into his heart and burned there. And
Yohseleh opened the door and ran out, he ran through
the streets of the city, and he ran in terrible haste
until he came to the cottage of the students. Here his
feet stopped. And his throat split open, and he cried,
" Messiah! "

But there was no loud voice about him; only his own
voice sounded and resounded slowly, and lived, and
was like the Voice whose Wings he had felt upon his
shoulders.

He forced his eyes to open, and made himself see.

There the aged ones sat on the threshold of the
house, in a long, curved row, and every mouth was
hard closed, and every look was far in the horizon,
and not a limb moved.

Then Yohseleh heard his own voice crying, " Now
and at once Messiah comes! " and he heard his own
voice resounding in the midst of the staring silence.
Then the soul of the boy flew upon the Wings of the
Voice, and lay within the breast of the first of the

students, and Yohseleh said, "Nachum, do you still remember how you fasted from one Sabbath to the other, that Messiah might come? Do you still remember how I came to you when you lay on the ground on the last day, and beat your forehead against the floor, how we cried and prayed together then? Now see, Messiah comes!" But the other was silent.

Then the soul rose and flew to the second student, and crept into his sleep, and Yohseleh said, "Elimelech, I saw you once bowed over a fire until your hairs fell into the flames, and your lips uttered the name, Messiah! I saw you once lift up your arms and shake your hands against the heavens, and your lips uttered the name, Messiah! Elimelech, he comes!" But the other was silent.

And again the soul went out, and flew to the third, and nestled in his hand, and Yohseleh said, "Yehuda, I heard you once when you spoke magic over the waters, and uttered dim words in the way of the wind. Your magic ran with the waters, and your enchantments flew with the wind. But now, Yehuda, hear me, now he comes, do you not hear him coming? Yehuda, let us go and greet him!" But he also was silent.

Yohseleh looked upon these aged ones, and his soul looked on them, and he saw them listening to a distant step. So they sat in a long, bent row, and listened to a distant step, and looked into infinity. Then loneliness came over Yohseleh and laid her cold hard hand upon the nape of his neck, and the nails of the fingers sank deep into his flesh, and the hand lay on his neck like a live, in-crawling mark. And Yohseleh saw how the Light went out of his own heart and faded from before his eyes. And Yohseleh felt how the wings upon his shoulders shrank, and fell away. And Yohseleh wanted to speak, but no voice came out of his throat. And Yohseleh wanted to go from there, but he could not lift his feet. And Yohseleh sat in the row with the others, and looked into the distance, and listened for a distant step.

So they sat together, until the stars came. And in his chamber the Baal Shem Tov struggled to force down the presence of Messiah. And as long as he continued the struggle, the sound of a distant step was in their ears. But when the sun was gone, the Baal Shem was empty of strength. And he knew that the heavens would not yield before his urge.

Then the binding power was loosed from the students. They arose, and returned to the city.

And Yohseleh stood in his house like a blind man, with unsteady feet, and his two hands wavered reaching out against the nothingness to left and to right of him, and his heart trembled like a sick leaf in the wind, and the mark of the icy hand was on his brow.

THE FALSE MESSIAH

THE STORY OF RABBI ISRAEL'S STRUGGLE TO OVERCOME
THE FALSE MESSIAH, AND HOW SATAN DEFEATED
RABBI ISRAEL

WHEN Satan heard Rabbi Israel beg for Messiah to descend upon earth, Satan the Enemy laughed and said, " I will send down Messiah."

Light has one great eye; but Darkness has a thousand arms; Light is One, and master of eternity; but Satan is legion, and reigns from each instant to each instant.

And now Satan reached forth one of his thousand arms, and brought down the false Messiah whose cursed name was Jacob Frank. He lived on earth, and announced himself as the Redeemer, the Son of God. With twelve disciples he went up and down the land of Poland, and wherever he passed, he left behind him the tumult of the end of the world. For everywhere Jews gathered their belongings together, and prepared to follow him to the Holy Land.

Then the Angel of Wrath came down and stood behind Rabbi Israel, and the fiery arm of the angel touched the shoulder of the Baal Shem Tov.

" What must I do? " said Rabbi Israel.

But the archangel was gone.

Rabbi Israel heard the cries and the tumult among the people, and saw the chaos that was like the end of the world, and he knew that it was his task to struggle against the false Messiah. He sought for his strength, but he was like a house that has been filled with the movement of living people, and is now empty and still. And he felt no power within himself.

Then he sent forth a call.

To each spark of his undying will that he had given out of himself during his lifetime, he called, " Return to me now, for I have need of all my strength for this combat."

His call streamed over the wide earth, into forests, and into obscure hovels, and into the very grave; for the rays of his power had gone into distant corners. From the souls of aged men, and from the souls of children, from the souls of scholars, and from the souls of simpletons, the sparks of the Baal Shem's inward flame arose, and they returned to him, until all of his powers were before him.

Then one small steadily burning flame spoke to him. " Master, I have come from the soul of a young scholar; and until you sent me to him, his life was miserable and drear, and he looked before him and saw only the grey unending plain, and the grey sky upon it. But now he sees the mountain of gold and the blue of brightest heaven, and his eyes are filled with joy, and his lips with melody. If you take me from him, misery will come over him once more, and the grey shroud. Then let me return, and remain with him; I am so small a power, Master."

Rabbi Israel remembered the wan boy who had come to him, and listened, and never spoken. He remembered how he had sent this very spark of his soul to the boy, and he said, " Return, remain with the scholar."

Then another spark, come from the soul of a dying woman, begged to be allowed to go with her into her death; and the Master did not refuse. Then from every side there arose voices, tiny like the crackling of forest leaves, and powerful as tall successive waves, first few, then many, until all about the Master there was a rush of pleading and crying: for the sake of a woman in childbirth, for the sake of the joyfully wedded, for the sake of blind and poor, for the sake of the simple-hearted: each spark of his power begged to return to the soul to which it had been given. At last Rabbi Israel raised his arms and said, " My children, go home, each to the heart you have come from, go."

And then the flames of his power left him again, and twilight came, and he stood watching the particles of his soul fading away like the dew that rises off the earth. He cast one long look after them, as the sun casts a lingering eye about the earth before sinking beneath the horizon.

Then the Master was alone, with what remained of himself. And he knew that what remained was little, for he was weak.

Yet he made his way up to the heaven of the prophets, and there he found his teacher, Rabbi Simeon ben Yochai, who had often come to him in his boyhood, at night.

" Teacher," said Rabbi Israel, " help me. Once I was ablaze as a seraph, but now I am only the shadow of a flame. Where shall I find the power to combat the falsehood of darkness? Where shall I find a soul that is a steady burning light, that I may set it to consume the darkness? "

Rabbi Simeon ben Yochai said, " Israel, I fear I may not help you. For my task is but to teach the Torah, and therefore I could never know that perfect Soul whom you seek, for he has no need of being taught the Torah: he is himself the Torah. Nevertheless, let us ask of Elijah. Perhaps in his coming and going over the earth, he has seen that one whom you seek."

At that moment Elijah passed through the heaven of the prophets. " The man whom you seek," he said, " is the shepherd Moses. You will find him in the Carpathian hills."

And without another word he lifted his feet, and returned to his labours on earth.

Rabbi Israel searched among the mountains. Untiring he went from peak to peak in search of the shepherd Moses. The beasts of the wilderness moaned before and behind him, and the thunders separated above his head; the wind was soft about his face, and the branches of the trees turned to make way for him.

He came to the top of a green hill. He looked down, and saw a flock of sheep in the pasture below him, like a small white cloud over the earth.

Between large rocks on the mountainside, a stream of water flowed.

The Baal Shem Tov saw a young shepherd walking among the rocks, and he knew that this was the shepherd Moses.

The Master hid himself, and watched.

The boy was beautiful; his neck was strong, his black hair clustered like the wool of a ram; his eyes were young and clear as the mountain stream. His face was alive with perfect joy engulfed in perfect love. He spoke aloud,

" O beloved God, show me what I must do because of You! If You had sheep, I would watch them day and night, for no reward but the joy of serving You! " The boy stood still. Then he looked at the stream of water. Suddenly he began to leap from one side of the stream to the other, dancing high over the stream, and singing his joy out loud.

"Beloved God! I am joyous because of you! For your joy, I leap over the stream! " And he sprang back and forth, back and forth, leaping with all his strength, laughing, leaping, and singing with joy.

Then Rabbi Israel knew that this was surely the perfect soul, untainted as the Seraphim, and pure as a column of fire. " Shepherd," he called, " come speak with me! " And he stepped out from his hiding place.

But the young shepherd, never stopping his leaping, called back, " I cannot speak with you now! I cannot rest from my toil! Every moment of my day is given over to serving my Master! "

"But you are only sporting, leaping over the stream! " the Rabbi said.

"This is not sporting," the shepherd said; " it is the only way I know to serve my God! "

Rabbi Israel answered him, " It is of that very God that I wish to speak with you."

The shepherd paused, and replied, " If that is so, I will come."

"There is one who is doing evil against our Almighty God," said Rabbi Israel. " You must help me combat that evil-doer."

The boy said, " But I am only an ignorant shepherd. I know nothing but to watch my flock."

"Let me teach you," said Rabbi Israel.

Then they washed themselves in the stream, and

they seated themselves on the rock, and the Master taught the Shepherd.

First he taught him the *aleph beth,* for the Torah is written in the mighty alphabet. Then he spoke to him of the dwelling place of the Glory of God in the Temple in Jerusalem, and of how the Temple was destroyed in the Enemy's flames. The Master spoke of the Shechina, the Glory of God that wanders since then like a sorrowing virgin, wanders lonesome and lost and weeping through time and space; and he explained to the boy how the tears of the sorrowing Shechina are gathered together to quench the thirst of all created souls, who, on drinking of her tears, become filled with the love of God.

Already the souls of the earth were cleansed and would return to their Creator, already the eternity of exile stood at the brink of its ending. But the vigilant power of Darkness stretched out a thousand arms and barred a thousand ways. Then Night sent his servant over the earth, in darkness the False one strode, and every soul that looked upon his formless countenance became pale, and lost its holy fire, and every ear that listened to his falsehood became withered forever, and lost to the sound of Truth.

"Where is that man!" cried the shepherd Moses. "I will go find him, and make an end to his evil!" And he arose, filled with Almighty power.

But at that moment the Enemy clamoured in the heavens. "Space is mine, and Time is mine!" he cried. "No mortal creature can come against me!"

Then a Voice floated outward over eternity, and the Voice was like a low wind over water. "True," said the Voice, all sorrowful. "You are the Prince of the Moment. Instant to instant, the world is yours, until you relinquish it to fall before Eternity! "

Satan cowered beneath that gentle Voice, his hulk shivered, and he hid his head in the ultimate chasm. But the Voice floated away and was gone. Satan raised his shoulders, he shook his giant form; he lifted up his arms, and reached his fists among the clouds, and knocked them mightily one against the other.

A storm broke over the earth. Black clouds split themselves upon the tops of mountains, thunders broke from peak to peak, and lightnings ran among the trees. Then the bells of all the villages were set wildly ringing, and all the world was in chaos.

The sheep of the shepherd's flock began to bleat, and run; they ran frightened everyways, and stumbled against the rocks, and shivered in the water.

The shepherd Moses ran from the side of Rabbi Israel. He ran one way and the other, gathering his frightened sheep, and carrying them to the safety of his cave. He lifted them tenderly, and spoke to them; he went far seeking for the lost ones, for he would not leave one of them astray in the storm.

And Rabbi Israel saw the form of the shepherd fading always further down the meadow, as he leaped after his straying flock.

Then the Baal Shem Tov knew that he had lost his needed help against the Enemy, for the Enemy was of today.

Rabbi Israel hung his head, for he felt very old.

THE HOLY LAND

THE aged Master lay asleep. And out of the night there came voices as from a distance calling, creeping into his sleep, and calling him. His ear awakened and listened. The sounds surrounded his bed with tones of unearthly pain that came from a hoary ancient mouth inconceivably far away. He could not understand the words.

Each night the voices came and lay on his heart, and by day he bore their pain within him. But one night the voices, trembling with the weariness of their long journey, came quite close to his ear. And he recognized them.

It was the mouth of the ancient land that spoke, and her words were filled with the shame of the fallen. It was the ancient vineyard, now become a stony hill upon which alien shepherds trod with hated feet from year to year; it was the temple wall buried under the earth, and the hidden Arc that groaned under the weight of immeasurable boulders; it was the stony hillside that once had carried high its waving trees; and it was the dried-up fountains of water.

They wept in their final agony, for their sleep must now turn into death. From moment to moment, each breath might be their last; unless the Hand would come and tear away the darkness, and free the beaten and buried Soul of the ancient land.

The voices prayed to the Baal Shem Tov, " Come,

and do not delay any longer. You are the Awaited one, whose breath will raise up the stones from our graves. The stream shall flow again, the forest shall rise up, and the vine become heavy with fruit. The fields shall wave in their garments of grain. Come, and place your Hand upon us! ''

Then Israel remembered Rabbi Chayim Ben Atar, the Light of the Living, who was in the Holy Land. And the Master knew that the soul of the Ohr Ha-Chayim was the counterpart of his own soul, and that if their two souls came together, then the all-powerful Soul of Man would be created, that might call down the soul of waiting Messiah.

Rabbi Israel answered the voices, saying, " I am ready."

But within his heart there was an emptiness and a sickness, for he knew the time was not yet come.

In those days there came to Rabbi Israel a letter from his brother-in-law Rabbi Gershon, who was with the Ohr Ha-Chayim in the Holy Land. And in the letter these words were written, " The Ohr Ha-Chayim sends his greeting to Rabbi Israel ben Eleazer. And the Ohr Ha-Chayim sends this message, ' When Rabbi Israel goes into Heaven, let him see whether every part of him, from head to foot, is in Heaven.' "

The words of the Ohr Ha-Chayim were as a wall before Rabbi Israel. For he knew that the Ohr Ha-Chayim did not wish him to come to the Holy Land.

Day and night, he was tortured with doubt.

At last he said, " I will go Above, and ask."

He raised himself into Heaven, and he stood before the Throne. He said, " The Enemy wanders freely over the earth, and there is none to combat his evil. The voices of my people cry unto me, and the voices of the ancient land weep about me. But alone I have no strength. In the Holy Land there waits the light of the living, Rabbi Chayim ben Atar. Unleash the bonds that keep me, give me leave, O Lord and Father, that I may go to the Land that calls me."

But the Heavenly Voice responded, " Israel, remain in your place."

Then Rabbi Israel turned to go out of Heaven. And his head hung down, and he saw himself. And he saw that he was not entirely come into Heaven. He saw that while his body moved in Heaven, his feet still walked on earth.

Then many nights the Baal Shem Tov lay troubled. The voices were in his ear, and the word of the Lord was in his heart. The crying of the voices rose above all the storm-winds that filled the air. There was a wailing as there had been on that day when Jerusalem fell.

The agony of the dying land prevailed over the Master, and drowned the command of Heaven. He arose, and said, " I will come."

The voices of the ancient land returned to that Place from which they came. And they cried, " Rise up you sleepers and you silent ones, prepare yourself, for your Redeemer is on his way! "

Then the flesh of the earth trembled. With one great sigh she shook her timeless sleep from herself. The call of life rose upward from the full heart of every sleeping thing, and a great tumult of joy arose toward the dawn. The deadened water prepared to run forth, and the corn ripened under the ground, and the juice of the vine was distilled. The stars over the ancient land widened like widening eyes, in that blue night of Expectation.

Rabbi Israel called his follower Rabbi Wolf, and together they prepared for the journey. Rabbi Israel's beloved daughter Dvorah went with them.

That day when the Baal Shem went forward, his joy and his singing were not with him. When Rabbi Wolf spoke of the marvellous end of their journey, Rabbi Israel answered only with a small, lost sigh. For now the voices of the ancient land did not sound about him, and he heard the Godward longing that cried in his breast with a wordless sound of sorrow. Each day, he carried the growing burden further on his way. He left city and country behind him, friends and believers in him.

Then they three embarked upon a ship. The ship was small, and it sailed out upon the middle of the sea.

Then, in the midst of noon, they saw another ship on the water. The ship came toward them, looming ever greater and higher, until its spars seemed to pierce the heavens, and its sides to be as wide as the waters.

The ship of the pirate fell upon their ship, and seized all those who were in it. They seized on Rabbi Israel, and on his follower Rabbi Wolf, and bound them and threw them into a prison. Rabbi Israel was separated from his daughter.

In the prison all was dark. Rabbi Wolf said, " Call upon the Name, and save us! "

Rabbi Israel said, " I cannot utter the Name."

Rabbi Wolf said, " All of the wisdom of the world is in your mouth. Rabbi, where is your power? You have but to move your little finger, and the demons will be destroyed, and we will go out of this prison and find your lost daughter."

But Rabbi Israel said, " All that I ever knew has gone out of me. I do not remember a single word of the Holy Torah, nor any sign of power."

He strove, and he could not do anything.

The chief of the pirates came into the prison and cried to Rabbi Israel, " You are a holy man, and a wizard. Perform some deed of magic, and fill our ship with gold! "

The Master knew of no way to fulfil the desire of the bandit.

Then the pirate became furious with anger, and drew out his knife. His fellows stood about him, and all drew their knives, to slay the imprisoned Rabbi.

Just then Elijah could bear no longer the suffering of Rabbi Israel. He came into the dark chamber, and stood by the fallen Rabbi, and whispered into his ear the first two letters of the alphabet. And Rabbi Israel said, " Aleph, Beth." These were the mighty signs with which the holy Torah was begun. And as he uttered the words, blindness fell upon the pirates.

They roared as they were stricken, and they fell about the room, and cut each other with their knives.

Then they ceased, and crawled to the feet of the Rabbi, and begged his forgiveness, and repented, and begged that their sight be restored.

" We will give you all of our riches," said the Captain of the pirates. " And we will leave off attacking the innocent ones."

" Only He who has taken away your sight can restore it," said the Baal Shem Tov.

Then that ship of the blind floated through eternal night upon the dreary sea.

In that darkness, a helmsman appeared, and guided the ship toward shore. No one knew whence he had come, or who he was. In dress, he seemed as a sailor. When he had guided the ship to a shore, Elijah left them. And the ship was near Stamboul.

As the pirates stepped from the ship, and touched the land, their eyes opened, and they saw. Then they said to the Rabbi, " Because of the help you have given us, and to prove to you that we are become honest men, we will release a captured maiden to you."

They brought the woman before him, and she was the daughter of Rabbi Israel.

Rabbi Israel was in Stamboul with his daughter Dvorah, and his follower Rabbi Wolf. The holiday of Passover came, and they had no way to observe the feast.

Rabbi Israel was filled with doubt, for everywhere he saw signs that his way was barred. Then he went out to visit the graveyard of the Jews. And there, at the grave of the great Rabbi Naphtali Kohn Tsadik, he asked, " Shall I continue on my journey to the Holy Land? "

But a voice replied, " Turn back, for the Time has not yet come! "

While Rabbi Israel was gone, a peasant came to the door of the house. The peasant said to Dvorah, " Will you take me in to observe the feast of Passover with you? "

Dvorah said, " You are welcome, but we have no food, and no way to observe the Passover."

The peasant said, " I will arrange everything.

He came into the room, and he brought a box upon his shoulders. The box was as large as the room. He opened the box, and from it he took a table, covered with a clean cloth. On the table were candlesticks, and plates, and matzos, and silver, and dishes bearing the bitter herbs, and the fish, and the meat, and all the necessities for the Passover.

Rabbi Israel came home. He sat down at the table and he ate with his guest, who was the prophet Elijah. And not a word passed between them.

There the daughter of Rabbi Israel died, while he still lived.

As he sat by the table, he was given English porter to drink.

He drank what was set before him. Then he said to Rabbi Wolf, " Some say this is a bitter drink. But it gives strength."

Rabbi Wolf knew that he spoke of the death of his daughter.

From Stamboul, they continued their journey.

The moon had many times changed over them, when once toward evening they came to the shore of the sea. There was no house or dwelling-place anywhere, and no sail on the water, only the sand, shimmering and wide, the beat of the water upon the sand, and the pale night overhead.

Then they both threw themselves upon the earth, that still breathed with the last warmth of the day; there they would rest until morning when they would seek a ship.

In the midst of the night, the Baal Shem dreamed. With his companion he was adrift upon the high sea, and his own coat was their vessel. The vessel was thrown to and fro by an unheard-of storm, and neither sky nor land was to be seen about them, only water everyways, high leaping, and broken.

The Baal Shem sought about him, but there was only the waters' deathly nearness. He sought within himself, and saw that everything was gone from him. He felt a weariness that was deeper than the depth of the sea. And in all his depth, there was emptiness. He saw his soul, and it was like the cast-off skin of a fruit, there was no juice in it, and no sweetness.

A great cry came over him, and his groaning was louder than the roaring of the storm. Then he threw himself down near his companion, and waited for the end.

In the night, as the Baal Shem warred with the loneliness of the waters and the hopelessness of his Soul, the Earth that had called him lay waiting. The Voices of Life buried within her called to the Voices in the air, and asked, " What do you hear? "

Then the sister Voices in the air answered, " A storm breaks, and he who should bring us our freedom struggles over the water."

As the Baal Shem lay upon the bottom of the Vessel, a lone and silent Thing, a Heavenly Voice, rose quite gently and began to speak within him, first simply, and as at home, but always swelling, and becoming mightier, until at last the Voice swallowed the howling of the ocean that was lost as a whisper within her call. And the Master drank the sound of the Voice of God.

The Voice of the Earth called to her sister Voices over the sea, and asked, " Is he nearing land? " And the answer came, " The compelling Word is upon him."

Then on that stormy sea of night a crowded ship appeared. The great ship was filled with pilgrims, who had sailed from the Holy Land to return to their far-spread homes; and now the sea rose mightily, and their ship was about to sink. They stretched forth their arms, and cried aloud for help. Then the Baal Shem Tov arose, and tied the sleeve of his coat to their ship, and drew them safely to Stamboul.

In the twilight of dawn, there was no more vision, and the Baal Shem Tov and Rabbi Wolf raised themselves from the sand. Their hair, beard, and clothes were wetted through, as though the sea had hurled them upon the shore. They did not speak, but avoided each other's eyes. They began to go on their way. Without word or sign they took their way backward, homeward the way they had come.

When they had wandered many hours, and the rising sun had dried their wetted garments, Rabbi Wolf looked timidly upon his Master, and he saw that the familiar holy light had returned upon his beloved countenance.

In the Holy Land, the Voices of the earth called, " What do you hear? " to their sister Voices of the air. And like the beating of wings of the angel of death came the answer, " We hear his steps receding in the distance."

Then the aged earth opened her mouth and spoke, " Now I will lie down and die." And she covered her face, and closed her eyes. And every thing returned to its place of rest, and prepared itself for death. And the stillness spread over the land, and in the stillness was hopelessness, and in the hopelessness was death.

But over the stillness a living Voice came that broke and scattered the death. And the Voice found the soul of the earth, and spoke to her.

" You shall not die, my friend. Earth of the Lord, you shall waken and live. Do not weep for him whom you called to you, for he is born out of One who must return, and the Hand of the Lord is upon his roots, to make Him live again in His time, and in your time, O my beloved."

HIS TORAH

WHEN the Baal Shem Tov was near his death, a student came to him with a written book and said, "These are your words, which I have written down. This is the Torah of Rabbi Israel."

The Master read what was written, and said, "Not one word of this is my Torah."

Before he died, Rabbi Israel said, "The holy men after me will be as the leaves on the trees. The Tsadikim will be as numerous as poppyseeds, and as great."

DEATH

AFTER THE DEATH

A MARVELLOUS STORY OF THE BAAL SHEM TOV, WHO
KNEW WHAT WOULD COME TO PASS AFTER
HIS DEATH

ON the day of his death Rabbi Israel called all of his followers about him, and gave each of them his future task. Some of the students he sent to other masters, some he made into leaders, and some he instructed to return home.

But to Reb Yacob he said, " After my death, you must go wandering from one place to another, and wherever you go, repeat my words, and tell the deeds that I did in my life-time."

Reb Yacob was not satisfied. " Why have you assigned me to a life of wandering and poverty? " he asked.

The Baal Shem Tov said, " Yours will not be a life of poverty, for you will be highly rewarded for what you tell of me. And when the time comes for your wandering to cease, a sign will be given you."

After the death of the Baal Shem Tov, each of his disciples took himself to the task the Master had meted out to him. And Reb Yacob, with his pack on his back and his staff in his hand, began to wander.

Wherever he went, people gathered about him. And he told them stories of the wonderful deeds of the Baal Shem Tov. The stories he knew were without number.

In every tavern in Poland, and in every little synagogue, Reb Yacob was known and welcome. In the taverns, he was given food and lodging; in the synagogues, money was collected for him. In this way, it turned out that his fate was not a poor one.

When he had wandered several years, Reb Yacob heard of a nobleman in Italy who lived for nothing else but to listen to stories about the Baal Shem Tov. " For every story that is told him," it was said, " he gives a gold ducat."

" I will tell him all the tales I know," thought Reb Yacob, " and then I'll be a rich man! "

So Reb Yacob took all the money in his possession and bought himself a horse. On the horse, he set out for Rome.

For six weeks he rode. And while he rode, he gathered in his mind all the tales he knew about the Baal Shem Tov, and all the sayings that he had heard from the mouth of Rabbi Israel.

On a Thursday night he came into Rome. He asked for the house of the nobleman, and he was shown a great palace that stood in a park surrounded by high gates.

When it became known that he had come with stories of the Baal Shem Tov, the Baron himself ran out to meet him, and brought him as a guest into his palace, and gave him a large chamber with a beautiful bed.

" On Sabbath, when we are seated around the table, you will tell us your stories about the Baal Shem Tov," said the Baron.

Reb Yacob didn't know what to do with himself. Wherever he turned, soft-footed servants bowed to him. He was honoured as a king.

" What should so rich a Baron want with stories of Rabbi Israel! " he wondered.

When the time came for the Sabbath meal, Reb Yacob was led into a great banqueting hall. Along the entire length of the hall was an endless white table. Around the table sat chassidim. And at the head of the table sat the Baron.

It was already known that a man had come to the palace who remembered every tale that was told about the Baal Shem Tov. As Reb Yacob came into the room, an awesome silence fell about the table.

He was placed at the right hand of the Baron.

The Baron said, " Did you ever see the Baal Shem Tov? "

" I saw him every day," said Reb Yacob. " He was my teacher."

" Tell me," said the nobleman, " what did he look like? "

Reb Yacob tried to bring the image of his Master before his eye. But strangely, he could not see him as he had been. So he said, " Like no other man."

Then he was frightened at what he had said, and he remained silent.

The chassidim ate the Sabbath meal.

At the end of the meal, the Baron said, " Now we will listen to Reb Yacob."

Reb Yacob opened his mouth to speak, and he could not think of a single word to say. He could not remember anything about the Baal Shem Tov, not one word that Rabbi Israel had uttered, and not one deed that he had done!

Reb Yacob looked about the table, and saw into all the eager faces, and he looked at the Baron, and he was terribly ashamed.

At last he said, " Let another speak first."

Then the chassidim began to tell stories of the Baal Shem Tov. Though Reb Yacob had heard these stories and had himself recited them hundreds and thousands of times, tonight they were as though he had never known them before.

After each chassid spoke, the Baron said to Reb Yacob, " Do you remember anything now? "

And Reb Yacob became more and more ashamed.

All of the chassidim had spoken. The hour was late. Then the Baron said, " Perhaps tomorrow, after the second meal of Sabbath, you will remember."

So it was at the second meal, and so it was at the end of the Sabbath.

Reb Yacob wanted to run away, he wanted to die. All during that day he thought, " The moment that Sabbath is ended, I will go away from here."

But he did not have another copper in his purse, and he was far from home, and he had forgotten everything he ever knew.

At the end of the Sabbath, the Baron said, " Stay another day. Perhaps something will come into your mind."

Reb Yacob sat all day alone in his room, but nothing came into his mind.

And still the Baron begged him to remain, and though he was dreadfully ashamed of himself, he remained another day, and a third day. And still he was served as though he were a king.

After three days he could no longer endure himself, and he said, " Let me go away."

The Baron brought him a purse of gold, and said, " Take this with you. And if you remember anything, return."

Then the Baron called his own carriage, and placed Reb Yacob in it, and instructed the coachman to take him as far as he desired to go.

When the carriage had started, something suddenly came into the mind of Reb Yacob, and he cried out, " Wait! I have thought of a story! "

The coachman turned the carriage. The Baron came running to the gate. And as Reb Yacob got out of the carriage, and as he walked with the Baron to the palace, Reb Yacob related what he remembered, for fear that it would go out of his mind.

" It is strange," he said, " that the one story I remember is something I never before remembered. And I do not even know whether I can recall the whole story. But I shall tell you as much as I know, for I am certain that you can never have heard this story from anyone else."

And this is the story he told:

" Once, in the week of Passover, the Baal Shem Tov arose, harnessed his horse to his wagon, and called to me saying, ' We must go on a long journey.' We got into the wagon, and we rode all night, and all night he was veiled in a terrible silence, for his Will was occupied in destroying the distance of space.

" In the morning, I saw that we were come to a city in Turkey.

" The streets of the city were festooned with banners as for a great holiday. People swarmed out of the houses, they were dressed in their holiday clothes. We drove through the festival streets. And suddenly we came to one street that was utterly deserted. It was in the midst of the city, and yet there were no banners displayed on this street, and not a person stirred upon its walks. The doors of all the houses on this street were closed, and every window was tightly shuttered. Every gate was locked. Not even a dog was seen alive upon that street.

" That was the street of the Jews.

" Rabbi Israel drove his wagon down that street. Before the largest of the houses, he stopped. He got down, and went to the door, and knocked. No one answered. He knocked again. Then we heard movements from within the house. He knocked a third time, and a voice screamed.

" Then he said, ' Open, in the name of the Unutterable Name! '

" Footsteps crept close to the door. Then the voice of an aged woman, in a frightened whisper, said, ' Who speaks? '

" He said, ' It is Rabbi Israel, son of Eleazer.'

" Slowly we heard the turning of the keys, one after another, in the many locks that were on the great door. At last the door was opened a crack, and an eye looked upon us, and saw that we were truly Jews.

" Then the door was hastily opened wide enough for our passage; a hand reached out and quickly drew us into the house. The door was swiftly shut, and locked with all its locks.

" The old woman said, ' Do you want to be put to death! Do you want all of us to be destroyed? '

" The Baal Shem Tov answered her, ' Have no fear.'

" It was very dark in that house. Rabbi Israel went to the window to draw back the curtains. The woman gasped in terror, and ran after him to prevent him.

'Rabbi,' she cried, 'do you not know that it is the Christian passover? In this city, on this day each year a Jew is taken and burned. If any Jew is found in the streets of the city, or if a Jew even shows himself in the window of his house, he is taken and burned on the cross in the market-place! And if no Jew shows himself, a Jew is chosen by lot, and sacrificed. Rabbi, you will bring death upon yourself, and upon this house!'

"But the Baal Shem Tov answered, 'Let me do as I must do.' Then he drew back the curtain from the largest of the windows, and opened the shutters that barred the wall. The window looked out on the market-place. And the Baal Shem stood in the window, and watched what was happening there.

"A great scaffold was erected in the centre of the square. On the scaffold was a Christian altar of prayer, and behind that there was a great wooden cross, and around the base of the cross were faggots piled ready for the burning of a victim.

"As we watched, a procession began to wind through the square.

"First came the ranks of horsemen, noblemen in armour of silver and of gold, bearing trumpets with silken banners.

"Then came the governors of the city, riding in splendid carriages, with wheels that were set with jewels.

"Then came the priests, in embroidered and gilded robes, bearing the marks of their office. And among them walked one, of higher office than all the rest, he carried a staff that dazzled all over with diamonds.

"And after the priests came music-makers, and

soldiers carrying lances, and richly attired people, and people of every sort.

" The Baal Shem showed me the mightiest of the priests, who carried the staff encrusted with diamonds, and said to me, ' That man is the bishop. Go down to him and tell him that Rabbi Israel awaits him in this house.'

" I went to the door. The woman cried, ' You are lost! They will seize you for their victim! They will tear you to pieces, and burn you! '

" But as the Baal Shem Tov had bidden me, so I would do, even though it were to walk into fire. I went out through the door, and I went down the deserted street of the Jews. No one molested me. I walked through the crowds, and across the market-place, and went through the ranks of the soldiers, and the monks, and the horsemen, and I came to the foot of the altar.

" The Bishop had just gone up on the platform. He was about to begin the service.

" I called out to him, ' Bishop, I have a message for you alone! '

" He said, ' Come up and tell it to me.'

" Then I went up on the platform where the wooden cross stood. I walked in front of the cross, and came to the Bishop. Then I spoke in his ear, whispering: ' Rabbi Israel, son of Eleazer, commands you to come to him at once! '

" The Bishop started. I thought he became frightened. Then, with every mark of respect, he said to me, ' Go back and tell the Rabbi that I will surely come to him in two hours' time.'

" I went down from the platform, again made

my way through the midst of the crowd, and walked
up the street of the Jews. Rabbi Israel stood waiting
at the door of the house. I told him what the Bishop
had said. The Baal Shem Tov became very angry.
' Go back at once! ' he cried. ' Tell him he must
come to me this instant! '

" The people in the house were in terror. They
clutched at my arms, they cried, ' Don't go! They are
about to begin the service! Once you escaped, but the
second time they will seize you! '

" Nevertheless I went again through the streets
and through the assembled multitude. The Bishop
was in the midst of reading the service. He was talking,
and his arms were raised. But I went straight toward
him. When he saw me his arms fell. Before I had
time to utter a word, he cried, ' I am coming at once! '

" Then he said to the people, ' The service is
ended! ' And he came down from his place, and
walked quickly away with me. I led him to the house
where Rabbi Israel waited. We went into the house.
Rabbi Israel received the Bishop, and took him into
a separate room. They were closed in the room for
three hours. Then Rabbi Israel came out and said to
me, ' We are ready to go home.'

" We got into the carriage and rode home."

" That is as much as I know of the story," said
Reb Yacob.

But even before he had ended speaking, the Baron
fell on his neck and hugged him and covered him with
joyous embraces. " I will give you half of my fortune! " he cried. " You have delivered my soul from
torture! "

Then the Baron said to Reb Yacob, "I was that Bishop to whom you spoke. Know, that I am descended from a long line of learned and holy rabbis. But when I was a young student, the evil spirit in me became strong, the Enemy entered into me and induced me to give up my holy studies, and to adopt the Christian faith. I became a priest. The Christians were proud that I had become one of them, and they did me great honour. They advanced me, and gave me high positions to hold. And always as I became more powerful, I became more cruel to my former brethren, and the more cruel I became, the more honour and gold the Christians showered upon me. At last I was made Bishop over that great city. And every year at Easter I burned a Jew upon the cross.

" Then, one night in a dream I saw a number of holy rabbis. They sat around a long table. And at the head of the table was the great Tsadik, ten times holier than all the others. And I saw that the rabbis around the table were my ancestors, though the Tsadik at the head of the table was not one of them.

" And on that table lay a poor shrivelled soul brought there for judgement. The rabbis were all of one accord, that the soul was doomed to eternal damnation, for it was entirely black, the evil spirit had utterly destroyed the good spirit within it. Then the Tsadik spoke to them and said, ' Let him repent, and the Gates of Heaven are not closed to him! ' The Tsadik touched the shrivelled soul with his little finger, and where he had touched it, a spot of white appeared. And the little spot of whiteness spread, and the soul became paler, its wrinkles began to unfold.

" That is all that I saw. But I heard my ancestors speaking among themselves, and I heard them utter the name of the Tsadik. His name was Rabbi Israel, son of Eleazer."

Then the Baron told me of that terrible day. " On the day of the sacrifice, I was filled with abhorrence for my task. I did not want to go to the market-place. But all the other Bishops of the land came and bowed before me, they presented me with a staff encrusted with diamonds and said, ' You are the greatest among us! ' I was vain and proud, I listened to their praises. I said to myself, ' This last time I will do it.'

" But when you came to me in the name of Rabbi Israel, I knew that my time had come. Still I was vain, and wanted to finish the service, to listen to the plaudits of the people. So I said to you, ' I will come at the end of the service.' But when the Baal Shem Tov sent you a second time to call me, I knew that I had to go at once. And I went.

" I will tell you what happened when I was alone in that room with the Rabbi Israel. He said to me, ' Sell all your goods, and divide the fortune into three parts. With one part buy your freedom. The second part give to the poor. With the third part retire to some far country, do good deeds, repent, and because of the holiness of your forefathers there is still hope that you will be pardoned your sins.'

" And Rabbi Israel said to me, ' When a man comes to you and tells you your own story, then you will know that your sins have been absolved.'

" When you came," said the Baron to Reb Yacob, " I recognized you at once as the messenger who spoke to me at the services in that city in Turkey. But when you could not remember anything, I thought, ' It is a sign that I can never be pardoned.' And when you started to go away, I thought, ' I am lost.'

" But now I know that the Baal Shem Tov has interceded for me in Heaven, and I am saved! "

Then the Baron gave Reb Yacob half of his fortune. And Reb Yacob knew that his days of wandering were over. He never ceased praising the name of the Master whose wisdom was a light on earth during his life, and after his death.

THE BOOK OF MYSTERIES

ALL of the knowledge of Power that the Baal Shem Tov ever possessed was contained in the secret book that he had received from Rabbi Adam.

After the Baal Shem had returned from his journey to the Ancient Land, he prepared for his journey to eternity.

Then Rabbi Adam came down to the Baal Shem Tov and said, " You have no more need of this Book. The Book is in your heart."

Rabbi Israel asked, " Who shall have it after me? "

That was the Book of Mysteries that had been given only to seven. It was given to Adam, and to Abraham, to Joseph, and to Joshua ben Nun, to Solomon, and to Rabbi Adam, and to Rabbi Israel, son of Eleazer.

And the eighth one to possess the Book of Wisdom shall be Messiah, Son of David.

The Baal Shem Tov and Rabbi Adam went up into the mountains. They found a great stone. Rabbi Adam touched the stone, and the stone split open. Within the stone, Rabbi Israel placed the Book of Wisdom. Then he touched the stone, and the stone closed.

RABBI NACHMAN OF BRATZLAW

GREAT-GRANDSON OF THE BAAL SHEM TOV

Drawing by Meyer Levin

THE TREE OF THE BAAL SHEM TOV

UDEL, the daughter of the Baal Shem Tov, had watched his scholars dancing at the Simchas Torah feast, and had given her shoe to Yehiel when he dropped his own shoe; then Udel and Yehiel were married, and of their union three children were born.

One was Baruch, who remained in Medzibuz, and became known as Reb Baruch of Medzibuz. Another was Moses Chaim Ephraim who became Rabbi of Salidikov. And their daughter was named Fiege. Fiege grew to be a woman of wonderful understanding, for in her was the spirit of holiness that had been in her mother Udel, and in her grandfather Rabbi Israel.

In Horodenka there lived a Chassid named Rabbi Nachman, who had a son called Simcha, which means joy. Simcha was not learned, but a simple-hearted man; and Simcha married Fiege.

Their son was called Nachman. In him there flamed again that strange and wondrous glory that had been in his great-grandfather, Rabbi Israel the Baal Shem Tov, for the stream of glory flowed unbroken through the generations.

Nachman was born in Medzibuz on the Sabbath of the first of the month of Nisan, in 1772. As soon as he could go about alone, the boy would creep away to the grave of his great-grandfather, the Baal Shem Tov, and by the graveside he would remain, sitting quietly, with the far smile of one who listens to pleasant words. A stream was not far away, and the burial place was soft with long grass and shaded with trees; it was not a place of death but of life; all day the sunlight shimmered among the trees.

The boy Nachman could read almost as soon as he

could speak. So great was his love of learning that when his teacher arose to leave at the end of their hours of study the boy would run and fetch his own pennies, and give them to the teacher, that he might remain a while longer and explain another page of the Talmud.

Then he learned of piety, and of fasting, and of the rigours of the purifying bath called the mikweh. On the coldest night of winter, the boy Nachman crept from his house, and stole into the house of the mikweh. He broke the ice over the water, and descended into the purifying bath, and remained there long, as in a pleasant summer stream. In the day, the elders saw the marks of his bare feet in the snow.

A great feast was held in the household in Medzibuz when Nachman reached his thirteenth birthday, and was ready to perform the service of manhood. At that time, his uncle, Rabbi Moses Chaim Ephraim of Salidikov, examined him in learning, and was astounded at the knowledge of the boy. " He will be the greatest of all the Tsadikim," his uncle said.

The next year, Nachman was married to the daughter of a wealthy merchant of Husiatyn, in Podolia, and he went to live in the house of his father-in-law while he continued his deep studies. It was then that he gave himself over to the study of the mysteries in the Cabbala, and of the writings of the great Cabbalist Isaac Luria, who lived in the Holy Land from 1534 to 1572. Bible, Talmud, and Cabbala he studied together. Often he performed the great fast from Sabbath eve to Sabbath eve, and purified himself by the severest rigours known to the ardour of the Chassidim, that he might be worthy to receive the deepest secrets.

Then he came to the truth that the Baal Shem Tov had known. And he found the living Joy everywhere, he heard the melody that hovered about the trees and stones, that came from the tall reeds that grew by the river. The woods became as filled with delightful mysteries to him as was the Book of the Zohar; and he went often into the forest, to meditate.

Sometimes he rode there on a horse; but he would get down from the horse, and walk about, and muse, and lose himself; and sometimes the animal would return alone to Husiatyn, while Nachman remained many days in the forest, without food.

Nachman had a small boat, and often he would float upon the river, and go close to the shore, and lie in his boat among the reeds.

After a few years, he left the village of his father-in-law and went to live in Modvediovka, where he soon became known as a Tsadik. Here, too, he was much in the fields and in the hills, for there he felt himself nearest heaven. "I go upon a way where no man has passed before," he said, "but even though the way is new, it is very old." And this is found later, in one of his wondrous fables.

It is told that once he had to pass the night in a cabin newly made of hewn logs. The following morning he was asked how he had slept. "I could not sleep," he said, "for there was moaning all about me all night long." No one knew where the sounds of moaning might have come from; but he knew. It was the moaning of the trees that had been cut down in their prime; of their logs the cabin had been built.

Nachman remained in Modvediovka until 1798. On Passover Eve, in 1798, Nachman remained long in the mikweh. When he came from the purifying waters, and spoke the words of the holiday ceremonial, " Next year in Jerusalem," there was deep meaning in his words.

That year he told his household that he must journey to the Holy Land. He had no means with which to make the voyage, for he was poor, having always given away whatever possessions came to him. There was not even money for his wife and daughters to live upon while he was away. Therefore he sent his wife to be a cook, and his daughters took places as servant girls, and Nachman went on his way on foot to Odessa.

There he took ship to Stamboul, and there again he took ship for Haifa. But the fleet of the Emperor Napoleon was in those waters, and the ship became entangled amongst the fleet, and there was great peril of death.

At last Rabbi Nachman came to Haifa, but among the Arabs he was thought to be a spy of the Emperor's forces, and they made great hardships for him. But on Rosh Ha-Shana of 1799 he was free in Haifa, and he remained the whole winter of that year in the Holy Land. He went on foot to the grave of the great Cabbalist Rabbi Isaac Luria, and to the grave of the father of Cabbala, Rabbi Simeon ben Yochai.

Then, he declared, a new life began for him. " All that has been before was as the life within the fruit before it is ripe." For now he saw the teaching of his great-grandfather in its truest light, and he saw that his own teaching had its roots in the same source as did the teaching of Moses. And he was not afraid to number himself among the greatest of the Tsadikim. " Since the Jews were dispersed from the Holy Land," he said, " there have been four great periods of learning, and at the centre of each epoch stood a chosen one. These are the four chosen teachers: Rabbi Simeon ben Yochai, Rabbi Isaac Luria, Rabbi Israel, and Rabbi Nachman."

He returned to Podolia, and there it was known that he judged himself the leader of the Tsadikim. But the other Tsadikim were strong against him, and hostile to his power. The great Tsadik known as the Seer of Spohlia mightily opposed the teachings of Rabbi Nachman, and was so violent in his attack upon the returned pilgrim that Nachman fled to the town of Zlotopoli, and at last journeyed to the powerful Rabbi Levi Isaac of Berditchev to ask for his aid against the Spohliar Zaydeh.

In 1802, Nachman left Zlotopoli for Bratzlaw, a city strong in Chassidim, and there he began his greatest work.

" A teacher must clothe his thoughts in wonderful raiment," he said, and so he began to tell his wondrous fables.

Many have their source in events of his own life; others in the books of mystery. The tale of the Wind that Overturned the World tells of a King and his Court, all together they comprise ten personages, corresponding to the Ten Sphiroth known in Cabbala, and those who know may find further meanings in those realms.

Rabbi Nathan of Nemirow, the most faithful of Nachman's disciples, often wrote down Nachman's tales as they had been told, word for word, " for each word is holy," he said, " and great mysteries are contained in these fables." Many tales were never written down, for Nathan was not always present; and many tales were repeated to him and written down after they had been told. The tales are so filled with hidden and visible holiness, that they may be related as prayers in the House of Study.

Rabbi Nathan remembered how some of the tales came to be told. " At the end of the year 1806," he says, " after the death of his son Solomon Ephraim, Rabbi Nachman journeyed to Modvediovka; and it was there that he began to relate the first tale, of the child that was lost. When he came home from Modvediovka, I visited him, and he said, ' On the way, I told this tale.' " And so the tale of the Lost Princess was told again, for it was the tale of a precious child lost to its father.

Another time, one of the disciples spoke to Rabbi Nachman of the upheaval brought into the world by Napoleon, " a man of low birth who has become an emperor! "

" How do you know," said Rabbi Nachman, " whose soul is within him? For it may be that his soul was exchanged in the nurseries of heaven, and is truly the soul of an emperor! " Then he began to tell the tale of the King's Son and the Servant's Son, that they might understand his meaning.

Once, it is remembered, he told a tale that lasted for two hours. All who heard it were so rapt in wonder and exaltation that when they came out of the dream of the story, they could remember only fragments of what they had heard.

On the eve of a holy Sabbath, the scholars were discussing a letter in which Rabbi Nathan of Nemirow had written that " they should be joyful." Rabbi Nachman heard their discussion and said, " I will tell you how once they were joyful." Then he began to tell the tale of the Seven Beggars.

Rabbi Nathan was not there, but a fellow-scholar hastened to Nemirow and told him that the Master had begun the relation of a new tale, more wondrous, more intricate than any of the other stories. And the scholar repeated to Rabbi Nathan the beginning of the tale. " I trembled with wonder and excitement," Rabbi Nathan wrote, " for I had heard many marvellous tales from the mouth of our Master, blessed be his memory, but none of them compared with this. So I hastened to his home." Rabbi Nathan ran from Nemirow to Bratzlaw, and remained there to hear the entire fable. For the story of the Seven Beggars took many days to tell.

In 1807 Rabbi Nachman visited several cities: Austroha, Zoslov, Dubno, Brody, and everywhere he was received with great honour, for his teachings were becoming known. But that year, consumption overtook him. He had been frail, and the journey to the Holy Land had used much of his strength. Now he was weak.

After Rosh Ha-Shanah of the year 1808, he went to Lemberg, and this voyage is veiled in mystery, but it is thought that he went to combat the teachings of Krochmal and Erter and the leaders of the movement for new learning and worldly speculation. Then he sent his faithful Nathan to prepare the publication of his teachings, in the book Likkute Maharan. This was done in 1808 and 1809, when Rabbi Nachman returned to Bratzlaw. But his illness was great, and he was made restless. He went from one town to another. In 1810, a fire burned down his house in Bratzlaw; and he knew that he himself was near death.

" I will not die here, but in Uman," he said. For once there had been a great slaughter of Jews in the town of Uman, and of the thousand who had been suddenly killed, many were not ready, and had not yet found strength for their journey to return to heaven; now their souls hovered wearily and homeless about the graveyard of Uman. But if a great Tsadik were to die in that town, his soul might lift all those remaining souls, and carry them with it to heaven.

Therefore Rabbi Nachman wanted to die in Uman. On the fourth day of Succoth in 1810 he called all his disciples to him and said, " When I die, burn all that I have written, and burn it upon the very ground where I lie."

When Rabbi Nathan saw his Master in the death agony, he cried, " Rabbi, Rabbi, in whose care are you leaving us? "

" I am not leaving you," Rabbi Nachman replied. " I shall remain with you, in my grave."

Early in the afternoon of the third day of the week, the Master, Rabbi Nachman, died. About him were his three most beloved disciples, Rabbi Nephtali, Rabbi Simeon, and Rabbi Nathan.

THESE TALES CONTAIN WONDERS AND MYSTERIES THAT
ARE HIDDEN IN SECRET MEANINGS, FOR NOT ONE WORD
HERE WRITTEN IS WITHOUT DEEP PURPOSE YET
EVEN THE SIMPLE READER UNLEARNED IN THE
SECRET OF WORDS MAY READ THESE TALES
WITH AWAKENING, FOR THEIR POWER IS SO
GREAT THAT NO MAN MAY READ THEM
IN VAIN, AND EVEN THE SIMPLE MAN
MAY SEE BEYOND THEIR FIRST
MEANING AND GLIMPSE THE
ETERNAL DELIGHTS AND
WONDERS IN THE
LIGHTNINGS
OF THEIR
TRUTH

THE LOST PRINCESS

AND HOW SHE WAS FOUND IN THE PALACE OF PEARLS

THERE was a King who had six sons and but one daughter; he loved his daughter more than any of his other children, and passed many hours in her company; but one day while they were together the princess displeased the King, and he cried out, " May the devil take you! "

There seemed nothing amiss that night when the princess went to bed. But in the morning she could not be found.

Then the King tore his hair for grief and guilt. " It is because of what I cried out," he said, " that she is gone."

Then the Second to the Throne, seeing the King in despair, arose and cried, " Give me a servant, and a steed, and gold, and I will go out and seek the princess."

For a long time he rode through waste land and desert in search of the missing maiden. Once as he passed in a desert he saw a road at the edge of the sand, and he thought, " I have ridden so long in the desert without meeting anyone. Perhaps the road will lead me to the city."

The road led him to a great castle guarded by hosts of warriors. The prince was afraid they would not allow him to enter the castle, but nevertheless he dismounted from his steed, and went up to them; and they allowed him to pass through the gate. Then he came in upon a magnificent courtyard, and saw a marble palace before him. He went into the palace, and walked through halls that were studded with alabaster pillars. Guards stood in all the passageways, but no one questioned him, and he went from room to room until he came to the chamber of the throne, and there a king was seated. Tables laden with delicate foods were along the walls of the room; the prince ate of the delicacies; then he lay down in a corner of the chamber where he might not easily be seen, and he watched to see what would happen.

Musicians played upon their instruments, and sang before the king; soon the king held out his hand and commanded that the queen be brought. Then the music became more joyous, and people danced in the court, and made merry, and drank, for the queen would soon appear.

When the queen came into the chamber she was given a smaller seat next to the throne; the wanderer looked upon her and saw that she was indeed the princess he sought. And as she looked out over the room she saw the man withdrawn into an obscure corner, and she recognized him. She got down from her throne and went to him and said, " Do you not know me? "

" You are the princess! " he said. " But how have you come to this place? "

" The King let fall an angry word," she said. " He cried, ' May the evil one take you! ' and this is the palace of evil."

" The King is grief-stricken because of what he has done, and I have sought for you these many years," the wanderer told her. " How may I take you away? "

" You cannot take me from this place," she said, " except that you first go and select a place for yourself, and there you must remain for an entire year, thinking only of my deliverance, longing and hoping to rescue me, and on the last day of the year you must not eat a particle of food, but must fast, and on the last night of the year you must not sleep; then you may come to me."

He did as she told him to do. He went into the desert and remained there an entire year, and at the end of the year he did not sleep, and did not eat, but returned toward the palace of the evil one. On the way, he passed a beautiful tree heavily laden with ripe fruit, and a terrible desire came over him to taste of the apples, so he went and ate. At once he fell into a deep sleep, and he slept for a very long time. When he awoke he saw his servant standing beside him, and he cried out, " Where am I? "

" You have slept many years," the servant said; " I have waited by you, while I lived on the fruit."

Then the wanderer went to the palace and came to the princess; and she cried, " See what you have done! Because of a single day, you have lost eternity! For if you had come on that day, you might have rescued me. I know that it is difficult to refrain from eating, and it is especially difficult on the last day, for the evil spirit was strong in you on that last day. But you must go again and choose a place and remain there another year, praying, and longing, and hoping to deliver me; on the last day of that year you may eat, but you must drink no wine, for wine will cause you to sleep, and the most important thing of all is not to sleep."

He went back to the wilderness, and did as she had told him to do, but on the last day, as he was returning toward the palace, he saw a flowing spring. He said to his servant, " Look, the fountain of water is

red, and it has an odour as of wine! " Then he knelt
and tasted of the spring, and at once fell to the ground
and slept. He slept for many years.

And in that time a great army of warriors passed
on the road, among them were mounted riders, and
carriages, and at last there came a great carriage
drawn by fourteen steeds. The princess was in that
carriage; but when she saw the wanderer's servant
on the road, she ordered the carriage to be halted,
and she went down and saw the wanderer sleeping,
and she sat by him and wept. " Poor man," she said;
" so many years you have sought me, and wandered so
far, and endured so much pain, and yet because of a
single day you have lost me, and see how you must
suffer, and how I suffer because of that day! " Then
she took her veil from her face; she wrote upon the
veil with her tears, and left it beside him; and she
got into her carriage and rode away.

After he had slept seventy years, the man awoke
and asked his servant, " Where am I? " The servant
told him what had happened, of the army that had
passed, and how the princess had wept over him. Just
then the wanderer saw the veil lying beside him, and
he cried, " Where does this come from? "

" The princess left it for you," the servant said.
" She wrote upon it with her tears."

He who was Second to the Throne held the veil
up to the sun, and saw the marks of her weeping, and
read of her grief at finding him so, and read that she
was gone from the first palace of the evil one, but that
he must now seek her in a palace of pearls that stood
on a golden mountain. " Only there, you may find
me," the princess had written.

Then the wanderer left his servant and went alone in search of the princess.

For many years he wandered among mankind, asking and seeking for the palace of pearls upon the mountain of gold, until he knew that it was to be found upon no chart, and in no land inhabited by men, and in no desert, for he had been everywhere. But still he searched in the wilderness, and in the wilderness he came upon a giant who carried a tree that was greater than any tree that grew in the world of men. The giant looked upon the wanderer and said, " Who are you? "

He answered, " I am a man."

" I have been so long in the wilderness," said the giant, " that it is many years since I have seen a man." And he looked at the man.

The man said, " I seek a palace built of pearls upon a golden mountain."

The giant laughed, and said, " There is no such place on earth! "

But the man cried, " There is! There must be! " and he would not give up his seeking.

Then the giant said, " Since you are so obstinate, I'll prove to you that there is no such place on earth. I am the lord over all the animal kingdom, and every beast that runs over the earth, from the greatest to the tiniest, answers to my call. Surely if there were such a place as you seek, one of my creatures would have seen it." So he bent and blew on the ground, making a sound that was narrow as the call of wind in the grass, and wide as the rustling of leaves; his call spread like spreading water, and at once the beasts of the earth came running, leaping toward him: the timid gazelle and the wild tiger and every creature from the beetle to the great elephant, all came, and he asked of them: " Have you seen a palace of pearls built on a golden mountain? "

The creatures all answered him, " No."

Then the giant said to the man, " You see, my friend, there is no such place at all. Spare yourself, and return home."

But the man cried, " There is, there must be such a place! And I must find it! "

The giant pitied him, and told him, " I have a brother who is lord over all the creatures of the air; perhaps one of them has seen this place, for birds fly high."

Then the man went further into the wilderness, until he found another giant who carried a great tree in his hand. " Your brother has sent me to you," he said. And he told the giant of his quest. The giant whistled into the air, and his cry was like the sound of all the winds that murmur and shriek high over the earth; at once every winged creature, insect and eagle, answered his call. But none had seen a palace of pearls upon a golden mountain.

" You see," said the giant, " there is no such place at all. You had better return home, and rest yourself."

But the man cried, " There is, there must be such a place, and I will not rest until I find it! "

At last the second giant said, " I have a brother who is lord over all the winds. Go to him, perhaps he can help you."

After many years the wanderer came to the third giant, who carried a still greater tree in his hand; and the wanderer told the giant what he sought.

Then the giant opened wide his mouth, and the call he hurled over the world was like the tumult of colliding heavens. In that instant, all the winds over the earth came rushing to him, and he asked them, " Have you seen a palace of pearls upon a mountain of gold? " But none of them had seen such a thing.

" Someone is jesting with you, and has sent you on a fool's quest," the giant said to the man. " Better go home, and rest yourself."

But the man cried, " There is, there must be such a place! " Just then another wind came hastening to the giant, and lay breathless and weary at his feet.

" You have come late! " the giant cried angrily, and he lifted the great tree to lash the wind. " Why did you come tardily to my call? "

" Master," the wind said, " I came as soon as I could, but I could not come sooner, for I had to carry a princess to a mountain of gold on which there stands a palace built of pearls."

The man heard, and was overjoyed. " Can you take me there? " he begged. The wind answered, " I can."

Then the master of the winds said to the man, " You will have need of gold, where you are going, for in that city all things are of high worth." And he took a wonderful purse, and gave it to the wanderer. " Whenever you put your hand into this bag," the giant said, " you will find it filled with gold, no matter how much gold you draw out of it."

Then the wind took up the wanderer and set him down upon the golden mountain.

The wanderer saw the palace of pearls that stood within a wonderful city, and the city was surrounded by many walls guarded by warriors. But he put his hand into his marvellous purse, and gave them gold, and they let him pass, and when he came into the city he found that it was a pleasant and beautiful place. Then he lived there for a long while, and there the princess lived, but in the end, with wisdom and righteousness, he took her home to the King.

THE BROKEN BETROTHAL

AND THE PORTRAIT OVER THE FOUNTAIN

THERE was once an emperor who had no child to rule after him; and in another land there was a king who also was childless. The emperor went on a journey in search of a sage who might tell him how to come by a child; and the king, too, went on such a journey. King and emperor stopped one night at the same inn, though they did not know each other; the emperor, however, marked the royal manner of the stranger, and asked him,

" Are you not a king? "

The king, too, had recognized the other as a man of high birth, and he said, " I am a king; and are you not an emperor? "

Then each told the other the reason for his travels, and they agreed that when they returned to their kingdoms, and if the queen of one gave birth to a son, and the other's queen gave birth to a daughter, the two children should be betrothed.

And afterward, a daughter was born to the emperor, and a son was born to the king, but the betrothal was forgotten.

As the children grew, each was sent to a foreign land to study, and it so happened that both were sent to the same teacher. The boy and girl met, and loved one another, and agreed to marry. Then the prince took a ring and put it on the finger of the princess, and so they were wed.

But soon their parents called them home, and the princess had to return to her father the emperor, while the prince returned to the court of the king.

The emperor's palace was filled with suitors for the hand of the princess, but she remembered that young prince from a distant land, and she would not have any of the others.

In his far country the prince was unhappy, longing day and night for his beloved; the king commanded entertainment for the boy in the palace, or rode with him over their domain, but the young man would not be cheered, and at last he fell ill of melancholy. Then the king asked the prince's servant: " Perhaps you know what troubles him? " The servant remembered the wedding, and told the king that the prince was married and longed for his bride.

" Who is his bride? " the king asked.

" A princess, the daughter of an emperor."

At this, the king recalled the betrothal he had made for his son before his son was born, and he was astonished to learn that it was indeed his betrothed that the prince had found and married. So the king wrote at once to the emperor to remind him of their meeting and of their vow.

But the emperor no longer desired such a union, and yet he could not free himself from his promise; so he sent a letter asking that the prince come to his court to be examined in his knowledge of government.

When the prince arrived in the emperor's palace he was not allowed to see his bride, but was seated alone in a room, and papers were brought to him, with questions of government. He was ill nearly to death with longing for a glimpse of his beloved, and one day as he walked by a chamber he saw her image in a mirror. Then he fainted of weakness and joy, and she saw him and ran to him and wakened him, saying,

" I will have no other husband but you! " And he said, " But what can we do while your father is against our marriage? "

They made a plan to escape together over the sea; then they hired a ship, and crept aboard at night, and sailed away. They were happy there, for they measured their love by the depth of the sea and the height of the firmament, and all the sea and sky was their kingdom of love. But one day the vessel came to a shore, and they said, " Let us go down on land for a while."

There was a forest near the shore, and the bride and groom went into the forest. They ran, and they walked, until they were weary, and the girl said, " Let me lie down by this tree, and sleep a while." She took his ring from her finger, and gave it to the prince saying, " Watch my ring while I sleep."

When he saw that she was about to waken, he placed the ring on the ground near her hand. She awoke, and they returned to the shore. But as they were going aboard their vessel she felt her hand bare and cried, " Where is my ring? " " I put it by you when you wakened," the prince said. " I'll go and find it for you."

She waited, while he returned to the forest. He wandered one way and another, and could not find the ring, and was lost.

The princess waited a long time, and then went into the woods to seek the prince, and she wandered one way and another, and could not find him, and was herself lost.

When the prince saw that he was lost he did not know what to do, but called her name, and she did not hear him; he wandered still farther until at last he came out of the forest to a city. He had no money, and he needed food, so he became a servant.

Meanwhile the princess found her way out of the forest and came to the shore again; there she sat upon the sand by the sea; she lived on the fruit of the trees; each day she wandered in search of her beloved, and at night she slept in the trees.

In another land there was a rich merchant whose ships sailed on every ocean, bringing him merchandise from all corners of the world. But he was aged, and he had an only son. One day his son said to him, " Father, you are growing old, while I know nothing of the ways of commerce; what will become of your enterprise when you are gone? Then give me a ship, that I may go and learn the buying and selling of merchandise, so that I may carry on your commerce for you." He was given a ship, and he sailed from one country to another, selling goods, and buying other goods. He was very successful, so that his cargo became richer every day. When his ship was filled with spices and silks and precious rarities he sailed toward home, but one day he passed close to a shore where high trees grew, and he thought the trees were a city, and desired to see that city. But as the ship came nearer he knew that they were only trees, and then he saw what seemed to be a human being perched high in one of the trees. He went out in a small boat and came to the shore, then seeing that it was a beautiful maiden who sat in the tree, he called to her to come down, and remain with him.

She said, " I will not come to you, unless you first

promise never to touch me before we are man and wife." This he vowed, and she came down from the tree, and was taken aboard his ship.

As they sailed on, he learned that the maiden was skilled in playing beautiful music upon many instruments, and that she could speak several languages. "Tell me, who are you?" he begged. "For I know you are nobly born!"

"Do not ask me who I am," the princess said, "for I may not tell you that until after we have been wedded."

One day he called to her and pointed to a nearing shore. "See, there is my city!" he said.

"You must go first to your people," she told him, "and inform them that you are bringing a bride who is a high-born maiden, then you must gather all of your people and lead them to greet me, and I will tell you who I am."

When the vessel was anchored she said to the young merchant, "But see, would you not give wine to all the sailors, that they may be merry for their master's wedding?" At once he brought up rare wines that he had secured on his voyage, and he gave the sailors drink. They all became drunken.

Then, when the merchant had gone to gather his relatives and bring them to greet his bride, all the sailors went ashore to make merry. As soon as the maiden found herself alone on the ship she freed the anchor, unbound the sails, and sailed away.

When the young merchant returned with his people, no ship was to be seen. "But I brought a vessel laden with precious merchandise, and a maiden to be my wife!" he cried. His father was angry and said, "You brought home nothing at all!"

" There are my sailors! " the young man cried, and he called to the sailors, " Where is my ship? "

They all lay drunk on the wharves, and when at last they were awakened they could not remember anything that had happened, except that there had been a ship, and they had been given wine, and now there was no ship.

The aged merchant was enraged, and shouted to his son, " Leave my sight, and never return! " Then the young man went out and became a wanderer over the earth.

There was a king who liked to be where the winds blew, and therefore he built his palace upon an ocean, and watched the ships sail by. This king had no queen, for no maiden in all his land pleased him. But one day he looked out from his palace and saw a strange vessel on the sea, and on the ship he saw no sailors, but only a single maiden.

As the princess beheld the palace she thought, " What do I want of palaces? " and she turned her ship to sail away. But the king had sent out after her, and her ship was brought to his city, and she was taken before the ruler. The king saw that she was beautiful, and desired her to remain with him.

" Then promise me," she said, " that you will not touch me until we are married according to law." He promised this, and she said, " Promise also that my ship will remain untouched, for it is filled with great treasure, and when our wedding comes I shall allow the treasures to be taken from the vessel, that all may see I bring you riches, and am not a maiden of the market-place."

This too the king promised. He sent messages to

many nations, bidding the rulers to come as guests to his wedding; and meanwhile he built a palace for the princess. She asked that eleven handmaidens be given her, and that they be daughters of high noblemen; eleven maidens came, and for each of them a separate palace was built. Every day, they sat with the princess; they sang, and made music. One day she said, " Let us go aboard my boat, and amuse ourselves." They went up on the ship, and she brought them some of the excellent wine that was on the ship, and the maidens drank, and fell asleep.

At once the princess loosed the vessel, and quickly sailed away.

That day the king looked out and saw that her ship was gone, but he did not know she had sailed upon it. " The princess will be heart-broken when she learns that her ship is lost," he said. " She must not be told suddenly." And he sent a messenger to find one of her handmaidens who might tell the princess gently of the loss of her ship.

The messenger went to the palace of the first hand-maiden, but did not find anyone there, and so he went through the palaces of the eleven noble maidens, and returned to the king and said, " I have found no one." Then the king commanded that an aged woman be sent to his bride at night, to tell her gently of the loss of her treasure ship. But when the aged woman came to the bed of the princess, she did not find the bride; and when the king heard that the bride, too, was gone from her palace, he was frightened and sad.

Meanwhile the noble fathers of the eleven maidens waited for the letters that they received each day from their daughters, and when the letters did not arrive

the noblemen came to the king's palace to see if all
were well with their daughters. They found that the
eleven maidens had disappeared, and no man knew
what had become of them. Then the noblemen were
furious, and cried, " Who knows what the king has
done with our daughters! " And since they were the
most powerful lords in that land, they decided that
the king should be put to death. But then they thought
again and said, " Perhaps he is not to blame, for his
bride is also gone." So, instead, they decided that they
would drive him from the kingdom, and rule in his
place. The king was taken from his throne, and sent
into exile.

And the maidens' ship sailed over the sea. When
the eleven girls awoke, they did not remember that
they had slept, but looked out and saw that the ship
was far from shore, and cried, " Let us return home! "
But the bride said, " Let us sail yet awhile. It is
pleasant here."

Then a stormy wind came up, and they cried again,
" Let us go home! "

" But we are far from home! " she said to them.

" Why did you bring us here? " the maidens begged
of her.

" I was afraid that the wind might break the ship,"
she answered.

So they sailed on, and the eleven maidens played
upon their harps and violins and flutes, and sang.

One day they saw a palace, and her companions
wanted to go near it, but the princess said, " I have
had enough of palaces. Indeed, I am sorry that I went
near the last one." So they sailed onward, and soon
they saw a hiding place upon the sea. They ap-

proached it, and found twelve pirates there. The pirates wanted to seize and kill them at once, but the princess said, " Who is your chief? " They showed her their leader, and she said to him, " What sort of people are you? "

He answered, " We are pirates."

" We too are pirates," she said, " but what you do by force, we do by cleverness, for we can make music and speak many languages. What good will it do you to kill us? Rather, take us as your wives, and we will bring you riches."

The pirates thought well of this plan, and came upon the maidens' ship, and the maidens showed them the treasures that were there. Then the princess said, " Let each man take his wife according to his station, and I will become the wife of the chieftain. But let us not all wed at once; let there be a wedding each day, and the chief shall be the last to wed."

To this they also agreed, and then she brought out her good wine and said, " This wine I had hidden until my true husband should come to take me, but now let us drink the wine! " She gave them twelve flagons of wine, and cried, " Let each man drink to all the others here! "

The pirates drank, and fell drunk asleep.

At once the princess said to her maidens, " Now go, and each of you kill her man." So they threw all the pirates into the sea; then they looked in the robbers' hiding place and found great stores of silver and gold and precious stones. The women said, " We will take no copper or silver, but only gold and jewels! " They took the silks and spices out of their ship, and filled it instead with gold and precious

stones. And then they decided to dress themsleves as
men, so they made men's clothing for themselves, and
wore it.

In another land there was a king who had an only
son; he found a wife for his son, and gave him the
kingdom to rule. One day the young ruler said to his
wife, " Let us go out upon a ship so that you may be
accustomed to the air of the sea, if by chance we
should one day have to escape that way."

They took a great ship, and with many courtiers
and companions, they went sailing on the sea. They
were merry, and sang, and drank, and became hot
with merriment, until the prince cried, " Let us take
off our clothes! " So they took off their garments, and
were all cool in the soft breeze. In jest they cried,
" Who can climb to the top of the mast? " The prince
said, " I will do it! " and at once he began to climb.

Just then the ship of the maidens came into the
same waters, and the princess espied the other vessel;
at first she feared to approach it, but when she saw
that it was filled with clowns and jesters, and could
not be a pirate ship, she drew closer.

Hair had fallen out of the prince's head, so that
there was a small round spot that was bald. And when
the princess saw the shining bald head of the naked
man upon the mast, she cried to her maidens, " Look!
I can throw that bald-headed man from the mast! "

They said, " How can you do it? You are so far
away? "

" I'll wait until he has reached the tip of the mast,
for then he will fall into the sea, while if he is lower,
he will fall back on the ship," she said.

They watched as he climbed, and when the man was at the tip of the mast, the princess took a burning-glass, and turned its rays upon the uncovered place on his head, and the rays pierced into his brain, his brain seethed, he let go his hold, and fell from the peak of the mast into the sea.

A great wail of terror arose on the prince's ship, for his people did not dare return home without their prince. Then some saw the other boat and cried, " Let us go near that ship, perhaps they have a physician who may help us."

They came to the maidens who were dressed as men, and asked if a doctor might be among them. " I am a physician," the princess said.

" Our prince has fallen into the sea, and he is dead! " they cried.

" Take him out of the sea, and let me look on him," she commanded.

They took the body of the prince from the sea; she looked at him, and felt his hand, and said, " His brain has been burned. He is dead."

When they found that the prince's brain had indeed been burned, they were amazed at the skill of the great physician and they begged, " Come back to our land, and be our king's physician."

The two vessels sailed together; meanwhile the courtiers of the first ship thought, " Let this physician marry the dead prince's bride, and be our king! " But they were ashamed to suggest to the queen that she marry a mere physician. Meanwhile the queen began to love the physician, for she did not know that he was in truth another woman; but she was afraid to marry him because the courtiers might not think it fitting for her to marry a man who was not a noble-man.

So neither the courtiers nor the queen spoke their thoughts, until the courtiers planned to make a festival, " and during the festival," they said to one another, " we can speak out."

So it was. They made the feast upon the physician's ship, and the physician, who was the true princess, gave them of her rare wine to drink, and they spoke their thoughts out loud. " How wonderful it would be if the queen married the physician! "

Then the physician said, " That would indeed be wonderful, but it should not be heard from a drunken mouth! "

The queen, too, spoke out and said, " It would be a beautiful marriage, if only the countrymen would consent to it! "

And the physician said, " Their consent might be asked, but soberly."

When they were no longer drunken they were at first ashamed to look at each other because of what they had said, but soon the word began to be whispered again, and at last it was said openly, " The queen will marry the physician."

So they came to the shore of their kingdom, and the people ran to meet them, for it was a long time since the prince had sailed away, and in that time his aged father had died and they were without any king. Now the people were told, " The prince died many days ago; but on the seas we took a new king to ourselves, for the queen has married again."

The people were happy that they had a king to rule them, and the king, who was really the true princess, ordered that a great wedding feast should be made in the palace, and commanded that to this feast should come all the exiles, and all the hunted men, and all the lost people who were in that land. This command was made known over all the kingdom.

Then the true princess disguised as physician and king declared that fountains of water should be made all over the city, so that whoever wanted to drink might find water; and she further commanded that a portrait of the new king should be placed over each well.

" Let watchmen be stationed near the portraits," she declared, " and if any man comes, and drinks, and looks on my portrait and recognizes it, and shows surprise or anger in his face, let him be taken and set in prison."

Everything was done as she had said.

And the first prince, who was her true husband, answered the command for lost people to come to the wedding; he came to the city and drank at a fountain, and when he saw her portrait over the fountain he recognized her, and cried out. Then the watchmen took him and put him in prison.

Then the merchant came, who had been her groom and had been driven from his home because of her, and he drank, and saw her portrait, and his face became clouded with anger. He was taken and put in prison.

Third, there came a king, who had been her groom, and had been driven from his kingdom because of her; and he drank, and saw her portrait, and spoke angrily; then he was taken, and put in prison.

The princess disguised as the king ordered the pris-

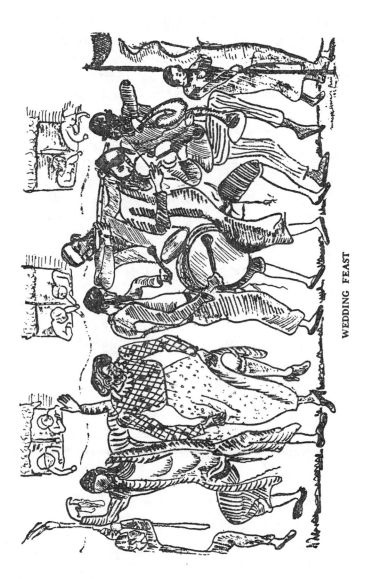

WEDDING FEAST

oners to be brought before her; they came, and did not recognize her because of her manly garments, but she knew them, all three. To one she said, " You, king, were driven from your land because of the eleven noble maidens who were stolen: here are your maidens, now return to your land and to your throne." To the second she said, " You, merchant, were driven from your home because of your ship that was stolen: here is your ship, take it and go home, and because it was borrowed from you for so long a time, you will find it filled with gold and precious stones in place of lesser wares." And to the last, she said as she arose and revealed her true self, " You, my prince, come here to me, and we two will go home together."

And so they returned to their own kingdom.

THE CRIPPLE

THERE was a Sage who, when he was about to die, called all his sons to him and gave them his last words. " Your task shall be the watering of trees," he said to them. " You may occupy yourselves with other things also, but you must never forget to water the trees." The Sage died, and left many sons. One among them was a cripple who could stand on his feet, but could not walk; and as he was unable to work for a living, his brothers gave him a share of their earnings. Their gifts were greater than his needs, so that little by little he saved a goodly sum of money. Then he thought, " I can now earn my own living by setting myself up as a merchant." As he could not walk, he bought a carriage, hired a servant and a coachman, and put all of his gold into a casket to take with him on the road to Leipzig. His brothers thought well of the cripple's plan to become a merchant, and gave him more money that he might thrive in his undertaking.

He rode forth on the highway. When the wagon came to a village the servant said, " Let us pass the night here " But the cripple wanted to go further, and commanded the servants against their wishes. They drove on, and lost their way in a forest.

Once there had been a famine in that land; then a man had come into the hungering city and cried, " Whoever would eat, let him come with me! " Many men ran to him, and he chose those of whom he had need. To one he said, " You might do as a workman," to another, " You might be a watchman," and so he gathered many clever young men about him and took them into the forest where he taught them to be thieves, for he said, " The highway to Leipzig and to Breslau passes through these woods, and many rich merchants go that way."

When the carriage of the cripple passed, the robbers fell upon it. The servant and the coachman, who had legs, fled; but the cripple could only remain on the wagon.

The brigands came up to him and cried, " Why are you sitting there? "

" I am a cripple, and cannot move," he told them. So they took away his casket of gold, and they took the horses from the wagon, and they left him sitting there alone.

The cripple ate all the food he had brought with him, but when that was gone he did not know how he would live. At last he threw himself from the wagon to the earth.

Night came; he was alone in that wilderness. There were strange noises, then everything was still, and he became so frightened that his remaining strength went from him, and he could no longer stand on his feet, but could only drag himself along the ground.

In the day, he was very hungry, and he ate the grass that grew about him. When he had eaten all the wild grain he could reach, he pulled himself farther along the ground, and ate again. And so he lived, until one day he came to a plant that was like no other plant he had ever seen. He had eaten many sorts of grass, but never found any that pleased him so much as this, and he decided to pull it out entirely by its roots. As he did so, he found a four-sided token tangled in the roots of the plant. On each edge of the token another message was inscribed. On one side, he read: " Whoever takes hold of this side of the token shall be carried to the place where day and night meet, and where the sun and moon come together." Since the cripple had taken hold of the token by that side when he found it in the roots of the plant, he was at once transported to the place of the sun and the moon. Then he heard the sun talking with the moon.

" There is a great tree that has many branches," said the sun, " and it is covered with leaves and fruit. Every twig, every leaf, every fruit has a power in itself. One brings wealth, another brings children, while still others heal all sorts of illnesses. If only that tree were watered, it would have a wondrous growth! But I am powerless to water the tree; instead, I shine upon it, and make it more arid and thirsty."

Then the moon said, " You are worried about others, but I have my own worries. For I have a thousand hills surrounded by another thousand hills, and there the demons live. They have no strength in their legs, for their feet are the feet of fowls; because of that, they steal strength out of my legs, and no strength remains in me. Once, I found a dust that healed my feet, but the wind came and blew the dust away."

The sun said to the moon, " I can tell you of a remedy. I know of a Way that divides into many ways; one is the path of the Tsadikim, for if the dust of that path is spread under a man's feet, and he steps upon that dust, he is at once a holy Tsadik; then there is a way of Unbelievers, for if the dust of that path is spread before a man and he walks a few steps upon it, he becomes an Unbeliever; and there is a way of Madmen, for the dust of that path makes men into Madmen. There are all sorts of ways, many of which heal illnesses, and among them is a path for those who have no strength in their legs. Holy men have been persecuted and led in chains by their over-lords, until their legs could support them no longer; but when their chained feet walked upon the dust of the healing way, they had new strength, and could walk. Go there, for the dust is thick on that path, and it will be a remedy for you."

All this the cripple heard; then he looked on the token that he held and saw the writing on the second side: "Whoever grasps this side of the token shall be carried to the Way that divides into many ways." He grasped the token on that side, and at once found himself at the parting of the ways.

Then he walked on the dust that was a remedy for crippled feet, and at once he was healed. He went and gathered the dust of all the different ways, and made separate packages, one with the dust of madmen, another with the dust of Tsadikim, and so with every kind of dust; he took the packages, and returned to the woods where he had been robbed.

First he chose a high tree over the robber's lane. Then he mixed some of the dust of Tsadikim with some of the madmen's dust, and spread the mixture upon the road, and climbed into his tree and waited.

The robber chief had sent some of his men out to spy upon the highway; they came, and as soon as they set foot upon the dust they were turned to Tsadikim, and they began to bemoan their days that had been spent in thieving and plundering, and they tore their breasts for the number of men they had murdered. But since the dust of madness was mingled with the dust of virtue, the thieves became mad Tsadikim, and one began to accuse the other of having brought them to murder, they quarrelled, and struck blows, and fought until they had killed each other, every one. Meanwhile the chieftain sent out other robbers to seek for those who had not returned, and they also walked on the same dust, and became mad Tsadikim, and fought and slew each other.

The healed cripple watched, until he knew that all the bandits had been killed, save the chief and one other. Then he went down from the tree and spread the pure dust of Tsadikim on the ground, and went back to his tree and waited.

The robber chief wondered why none of his band had returned, until at last he went out with his companion to find them. But as soon as he set foot upon the path he became a true Tsadik, and he held his head and moaned for the evil that he had done, and he tore his breast because of the murders he had committed, and he cried aloud over his sins, and begged for punishment.

Now the healed cripple came down from the tree. The chieftain ran to him begging, " Pronounce a punishment upon me! "

" First," the cripple said, " return the casket of gold that you took from me."

Each thing that was robbed, and the name of the person from whom it had been taken, was recorded in the book of the chieftain. " I'll give you your casket at once! " he cried, " and I'll give you all the other treasures that I have stolen! Only tell me how I may be punished! "

" You must go to the city and say that you are he who once came in time of famine and called out for men to follow you, and you must give account of the robberies you have done, and the people you have killed, and the treasures you have stolen. That is your punishment," the cripple said.

Then the robber gave him all the stolen treasures, and they went into the city, where the robber cried out all his sins.

" Let us hang him," said the people of the city, " as an example for all other robbers." So he was hanged.

Then the healed cripple thought, " I will go to the two thousand mountains of the moon." And he took hold of another side of the token, and came to a place from which he could see all that happened in those mountains; he saw that they were filled with thousands of myriads of demon families whose countless numbers grew ever greater, for demons are fruitful and multiply as men. He saw their King seated upon a throne such as no man sits upon, while his subjects tumbled and sprang before him, and jested with wild laughter, telling him of their pranks.

" I tore an arm from a man! " one demon cried.

" I tore a leg from a man! " another demon boasted.

" I tore a babe from its mother! " cried a third.

And they laughed and were joyous.

But meanwhile the cripple saw two elderly demons,

father and mother, walking and weeping. Then they were asked why they wept.

" Each day our son would go out on his way," they said, " and return in his time; but today the time is long gone by, and he has not returned." Then they were brought before the King of Demons, and he commanded his servitors to go out over all the earth to find the missing one.

As the mother and father went from the King, they met a younger demon who had gone forth with their son, and they asked for news of their son.

" He is in torment! " the young one cried. " For we had an island on the sea, but an Emperor came who owned that island, and he wanted to build a palace there. The Emperor began to build foundations, but your son said, ' Let us tear his strength from him! ' So we took away his strength. The Emperor called all his doctors, but they could not bring back his strength; then he called his magicians, and among them there was one who knew the Name of your son's family of demons, though he did not know of mine. By that Name, the magician caught your son, and he keeps him now in his power, and never ceases tormenting him."

The escaped one was brought before the King of Demons, and he told his story again. Then the great Demon said, " Let the Emperor's strength be returned to him, that the boy may be freed."

But the youthful demon said, " Among us there was one who had no strength, and we gave him the strength that we took from the Emperor."

" Take the strength back from your friend, and

return it to the Emperor! " the King of Demons commanded.

" But our friend has become a Cloud," the youthful one said.

" Send a messenger to the Cloud, and command him to come before me! " the King of Demons decreed.

Then an emissary was sent for the Cloud. And the cripple, who had listened to the Demons all that while, thought, " I will go after the messenger, and see how an evil spirit may turn into a cloud." He went, and came to a city that lay under a vast and darksome cloud. Then the cripple asked a man in the city, " Is your city always so dark and cool? "

" There never before was a cloud over our city," the man replied. " But a short time ago this darkness came and covered the sky."

Just then the Demon's emissary called to the Cloud, and it went away with him.

" I'll follow again, and hear what they say! " the cripple thought. So he followed the Cloud, and heard it talking with the messenger.

" How did you come to take the form of a cloud over that city? " the messenger asked.

The Cloud answered, " Here is the story. Once there was a Sage who lived in a kingdom whose ruler was a terrible unbeliever, and that ruler demanded that all of his people become unbelievers. Then the Sage called together all his kin and said, ' You see that the King would make all the nation into unbelievers. Some of our own kind have already followed him. Then let us go into the desert, in order that we may not be torn from our faith.' All agreed, and the Sage uttered a Name, and they found themselves in a wilderness. But that desert did not please him, so again he uttered a Name, and they were brought to a second wilderness; this also failed to please him; a third time he spoke the Name, and now they were brought to a desert that pleased him. And that desert was not far from the two thousand mountains of the moon.

" When they had chosen their place, the Sage drew a circle about them; and no power might break through that circle. There let us leave the Sage and all his family," the Cloud said, " while we speak of the Tree.

" There is a Tree that stands just beyond the two thousand mountains, and if that Tree were watered, all of our demon kind would come to an end, for there would be no more ill on earth. In order to keep the earth's water from coming to the Tree, numbers of demons stand near that Tree and dig the earth, day and night, to make a pit around it."

" Why must they remain forever digging? " the messenger asked. " Would it not suffice to dig the pit once? "

The Cloud answered, " There are whispering demons among us who go about the earth and whisper and murmur to one king and another, until they bring the kings to make war upon each other; then the earth quakes with war, and the soil tumbles back into the pit that is digged about the Tree. Then water might come to the Tree, and end our lives. So we must stand forever digging the pit, that no water may come to the tree.

" Whenever a King is crowned among us, and

demons tumble and make merry before him, and tell him how they have torn arms and legs from men, and torn apart infants, then the King becomes joyful and his heart feels strong; he gathers about him all the lords of his kingdom, and walks over the two thousand hills with them; he leads them to the place of the Tree, and they try to see who may have the strength to uproot that Tree and put an end to the danger that stands against our kingdom. The King strengthens his heart that he may not fear the Tree, but as soon as he approaches it the Tree sends forth a great cry, and the King is frightened, and must turn back.

" Once there was a great King among us who held a marvellous feast, and when he had heard of the deeds of all his demons his heart was filled with strength, and he went out with his princes to pull up the Tree by its roots; but as he came to it the Tree cried out so terribly that even he was frightened, and he turned away, but with awful anger. As he turned, he saw men in the wilderness, for the Sage and his family lived there. Then the King sought to vent his anger upon them, and he called his demons, and sent them to tear apart that family.

" As the people saw the demons coming they were frightened, but the Sage said, ' Have no fear.'

" The demons could not approach the people because of the magic circle about their place. The King sent more and more armies against the Sage's people, but not all the warriors among all our myriads could pierce the Sage's circle. At last the King, in great wrath, strode to the border himself, and beat against it with his sword, but he could not get in. And when his fury was spent, he begged, ' Let me come in within your circle.'

" At once the Sage replied, ' Since you ask, I will let you in among us. And since a King must not walk alone, you may bring a companion with you.' Then the Sage opened a little door, and allowed them to come in, and locked the circle after them.

" The King cried, ' How do you come to live upon my land? '

" ' It is not your land,' the Sage replied, ' but mine.'

" The King said, ' Are you not afraid of me? '

" The Sage answered, ' I have no fear of you.'

" ' You have no fear of me? ' the King cried out again, and he drew himself up until his form towered to the very heavens. But the Sage replied, ' I have no fear of you at all; but if I wish it, I can make you fear me.' Then he went away and prayed, and at once a great cloud formed, and there was thunder in the heavens, and thunder is the death of demons."

All this the Cloud told the messenger. Then he continued:

" All the princes who stood outside the circle waiting for the King were killed at once by that thunder; and only the King and his companion remained alive.

" Then the King begged the Sage to put an end to the thunder; and the thunder ceased. The King was grateful and said, ' Since you are indeed a noble man, I will give you a book in which the Names of all our families of Demons are written. Among mankind there are masters of Names who know how to call one family, and not even all of that family. But you will know us every one, for even the Names of the new-born are written in the book of the King.' Then the

King sent his companion, and thus it was shown how wise the Sage had been to cause him to bring a companion; and the book was brought. The Sage opened the book and saw that it was filled with thousands of myriads of Names.

" The King promised also that not one of the Sage's people should ever be harmed by demons. ' I will keep in my kingdom a portrait of each of your family,' the King said, ' and whenever a new babe is born among you, his image too shall be with us, so that the demons may know not to harm him.' Then the King went out of the circle, and returned into the hills.

" At last the time came for the Sage to leave the world, and he called his children to him and said, ' I leave you this book of Names, but know that although I have the power to use this book in purity, I have not made any use of it; and you also, even if one of you may have the power to use it in purity, let him make no use of it, but take his strength only from his belief in the Wonderful Name.'

" The Sage died, and his grandson became heir to the book. He, too, had the power to use it in purity, and yet he did not do so, but relied only upon the power of the Wonderful Name.

" But once the evil whisperers came to him, and spoke to him of his daughters. ' You have grown daughters, and no wealth with which to dower them. Make use of the book,' they said. He did not know that they who spoke were demons, but believed it was the voice of his own heart. Nevertheless he was uneasy, and he went to the grave of his grandfather, the Sage.

" He called to the grave and said, ' Grandfather, I

remember well your command that the book should never be used, and I have until now relied upon my belief in the Wonderful Name. But now my heart tells me to make use of the Demon's book! '

" Then his grandfather spoke to him from the grave, saying, ' Even though you have power to use the book in purity, shun it, and rely only upon your belief in the Wonderful Name. Then the Name will help you.' The grandson returned, and did not touch the book.

" Then there came a day when the Emperor of that land where the Sage's family lived became sick, and no physician could cure him, for he suffered from the heat that was over his city. At last he commanded the Jews to pray for him to make him well.

" Then there was consternation among the Sage's people, for they feared the wrath of the Emperor if they could bring no cure for his illness.

" But our own King of Demons learned that the Sage's grandson had never made use of the book of our Names, although he had power to do so in purity. And our King was grateful to that man, who had power over us, but brought no hardship upon us. And our King desired to reward the Sage's grandson, and all his people, by helping them out of their danger. So the King commanded me to become a cloud and to hang over that city, that it might become cool, and that the Emperor might be healed of his illness. Therefore I became a cloud."

The cripple heard the Cloud tell this story, and then he saw the Cloud brought before the King of Demons. And the King took away all the Cloud's strength and returned it to that first Emperor who was building a palace on his island. That Emperor's magician released the imprisoned young demon, who returned to his father and mother. But the young demon was weak because of the punishment he had undergone, and in wrath at the magician who had tormented him. So he plotted with all his family of demons to revenge himself upon that magician.

But there are Whisperers among the demons; they heard the plot and warned the magician. He called to him other wizards who knew the Names of families of demons, and they made ready to do battle.

Then, in the two thousand hills of the moon, it was learned that the Whisperers had betrayed their own kind. And there came a division among the demons; some were with the Families, and some were with the Whisperers.

Once it happened that several of the Whisperers had to stand watch together with several demons of of the Families. Then the Demons of the Families made a plot, and went to the King with a false accusation against the Whisperers, saying they had whispered treason. The King believed the accusation, and at once caused the death of several of the Whisperers.

Now all the remaining Whisperers were furious at this injustice, and they went up on earth and brewed trouble among all the kings of earth, so that there was hunger, and pestilence, and death everywhere among men and among demons of the earth; then the whole world shook with the violence of battle, and earthquakes came of war. And then the walls of the Demon's pit fell inward, and the soil filled the pit and pressed against the Tree, and the water passed through the earth to the Tree, and the Tree drank.

And all the Demons perished.

"*And he shall be like a tree planted by the rivers of water, that bringeth forth his fruit in his season; his leaf also shall not wither; and whatsoever he doeth shall prosper.*

"*The ungodly are not so: but are like the chaff which the wind driveth away.*"

THE BULL AND THE RAM

ONCE in a far country there was a king who issued a decree commanding all the Jews in his kingdom to be converted to his faith; those who would not be converted lost all their possessions and were driven into exile.

Many Jews gave up all their riches and in poverty fled the land; others could not part with their possessions, and became converted; and still others pretended to become converted, but in secret continued to be Jews. Every day they would go to a synagogue hidden underground, and they would bind over their arms the phylacteries made of bull's hide, and put over their shoulders the prayer-shawl with fringes of ram's wool, and they would say the morning prayer. There, in secret, they performed the rites of marriage, of circumcision, of holiday.

After a short time, the king died, and his son ruled. The son was a clever tyrant; he governed well, but with a strong hand; and those powers that had formerly belonged to the noblemen, he took to himself, until the noblemen of the kingdom came to hate him bitterly for robbing them of their ancient rights. Then the barons came together and formed a conspiracy. " We will murder the king, and all his family, and we will rule in his stead, " they whispered, one to the other.

But in the band of noblemen there was one of the wealthy Jews who had only pretended to be converted in order to remain in the kingdom, and now he thought: " Of what use is my life of lies? I pre-

CIRCUMCISION

tended conversion because I could not part with my riches, or bear to leave the court of the king. But if the king is killed the country will fall into turmoil and I will lose everything, for a country cannot exist without a king, and one man will swallow up another."

So he decided to go secretly to the king and warn him of the plot against him. The king set spies, to make sure that the former Jew had told the truth, and the night came on which the noblemen had planned to murder the young king, his infant son, and all the royal family.

Then the conspirators crept into the king's chamber, with their knives drawn; but the king lay awake, and his spies were hidden all about the room; the murderers were captured, and they were all punished as befitted their intended crime. But the king remembered the converted Jew who had warned him of their plot, and he desired to reward the Jew.

"What reward shall I give you?" he asked of the loyal man. "I cannot give you nobility, for you are already a nobleman; and gold would be no gift to you, for you are already exceedingly rich. Then tell me what you want me to do for you, and I will do it."

The nobleman said, "Will you indeed give me whatever I ask?"

"Whatever you ask!" declared the king.

"Will you swear by your crown and your kingdom?"

The king placed his hand upon his crown and said, "I swear it by my crown and by my kingdom."

"Then," said the pretended convert, "let me again be a Jew before all the world, let me wear my prayer-shawl and phylacteries in the morning, and practise my religion in freedom."

When the king heard this he was angry, for in all his land there was not one Jew who dared wrap himself in a praying-shawl, or wear phylacteries against the former king's decree. Nevertheless, as he had sworn by his crown and his country, he was forced to grant the Jew his request.

The next morning, and every day thereafter, the Jew stood where all might see, and wrapped in the splendour of his praying-shawl, with the phylacteries on his arms and forehead, he prayed as his fathers had prayed.

And there came a time, and that king died, and his son reigned in his stead. Now the son remembered how his father had been a tyrant, and how the noblemen had plotted to kill him, so the son instead was a mild and good king, and a learned man; his ntry prospered, and he took many other count es and ruled over them.

When a son was born to him in his turn, the king remembered the plot to kill all his father's family, and he wanted to make his crown secure for his own son, so he called all the seers of the kingdom into his palace and said, " Tell me, by what power may my seed be cut off, that I may be warned against it."

The seers consulted the stars, and answered, " No power can destroy your family, but you must beware of the bull and the ram."

Then this was written in the Book of the King: " Beware of the Bull and the Ram." When he was old, the king gave the book to his son, and he said to his son, " Rule gently, and with wisdom." Then the third king died, and his son ruled in his stead.

But the fourth king was like the second king, harsh in his ways, and a tyrant; he too captured many other nations and added them to his kingdom. He remembered the warning in the Book of Kings, and in order to make sure that no harm could come to him and his seed, he commanded that every bull and every ram should be driven from his kingdom. And this was done, until not a bull or ram remained in all that land.

Then the king thought of a plan by which he might capture all the world, and without a single battle. For this king too was very learned, and he knew that the whole world was divided into seven parts, while seven planets went round the heavens, one to light each day, and each planet went with one of the world's seven continents; and he knew that each of the seven parts of the world possessed one of the seven kinds of metal of which the world is made, so that each metal possessed the light of the planet that went with its continent!

Then the king sent messengers to all parts of the earth, commanding that the seven metals of the earth be brought to him. They brought him silver and copper and gold, and with the gold they brought all the golden portraits of all the kings on earth; then they brought all the other metals, and he took them, and had them made into the figure of a man. The head of the figure was of gold, the throat was of silver, and the trunk of the body and each limb was of another metal, so that in all the image was composed of the earth's seven metals. The king placed the statue upon the edge of a high mountain, and all the seven planets of the heavens turned around the image, and shone their light into it.

Then all over the world people knew that the image had a wondrous power, for if any man needed to know whether to do or not to do a certain thing, he would travel until he came to the statue on the mountain, and he would place himself before the part of the statue that was made of the metal of that part of the earth from which he came, and he would ask the statue whether or not he should do this thing. If the metal that was from his continent shone with light, then the answer was " yes! " and if the metal remained dark, its answer was " no! " And through the fame and power of this marvellous image, all the world came and paid homage to the king who had caused it to be made; and they brought him all their riches.

But yet he was not satisfied. And one night when the sky was dark with great clouds that stumbled one over the other, and the air was dank and cold, the king went out alone from his palace and climbed to the top of the mountain. There he stood before the giant that was made of the earth's seven metals. The shape could hardly be seen in the darkness. The king placed his hands upon it; the metal was cold, and his fingers felt frozen against it.

Then he cried out, " You that contain all riches and all wisdom! Answer me, can I become ruler of this world? "

Suddenly the great image became a column of glowing white fire; it was as though lightning stood before him. The face, the limbs, and every part of the moulded form, the gold, the silver, and every other metal glowed brilliantly in the cold darkness, and overhead amongst the clouds there was a terrific clash as of hailing trumpets.

The king was frightened, and then he was pleased, and he cried, " How may I become ruler of the world? "

Then the statue opened its golden mouth, and it spoke: " Humble the mighty, and raise the lowly."

It was silent; and the glow went out of the image. The king shivered. All about him was dark, and the air pressed against him as earth in a pit. He found his way back to the palace.

The words spoken by the golden mouth remained with him. " It is well," he thought, " if I cut down the mighty, for no one will remain to have power against me." Then he issued a decree. From all the noblemen, he took away their nobility; he dismissed all generals from their commands; he deprived the judges of their power to judge; and he made his governors into slaves. Even those men who had their titles of nobility from ancient times, and those officials who had won their honours from his father and his grandfather, lost their titles and their rights; all the mighty were cut down.

" So," the king thought, " I alone must have power. And I will raise no lowly man into power."

Then he called before him all those who remained who still had honours and rights, the proud lords of ancient lineage, and the mightiest generals: those among them who would not come were brought by force, and they were thrown upon their knees before him, and all were deprived of their rank. But among those whose names were written in the former king's book of honour was that Jew who had saved the royal family. And when this man was brought before the fourth king of that family, he was asked:

" What title have you? "

" None," the Jew replied.

" Then what command have you? "

Again he answered, " None."

" Then what privilege have you, that makes you higher than other men? "

" I am not higher than other men," said the aged Jew. " Only, many years ago, in the time of your highness's grandfather, I learned of a plot to kill the king and all the royal family, and because I warned him of that plot the king gave me back the right to worship freely and openly as a Jew, and to wear my praying-shawl and phylacteries, as my father had done before me."

The young king said, " This privilege shall be taken from you. You must become a convert, as you were."

So the aged Jew was forced once more to become a convert. Once more he would have to hide his worship in holes underground, and whisper his prayers in fright. Then as he left the court, he clutched the edges of his praying-shawl in one hand, and his phylacteries in the other hand, and he raised his eyes to heaven, and he uttered a curse. " Cursed be he! " he cried upon the tyrant king, " and cursed be all his seed. May they be cut off from the earth, so that no particle of their cruel flesh, and no drop of their tyrant blood, remain to torture mankind! " And that night, in a hidden dungeon, behind barred doors, he prayed.

And the king dreamed. He dreamed that he lay beneath the heavens; it was night, and the black sky pressed close upon him, the sky was close as the roof of his chamber. In the sky were the twelve beasts of the zodiac, each creature the sign of a month of the year. The crab and scorpion were there, and the lion, and all the others; but two of the twelve glowed with a light stronger than that of all the other ten. He saw them. They were bull and ram. And as he looked upon them, the bull and the ram opened their jaws, and laughed. He saw their strange, brutal laughter, but he could not hear anything.

The king shivered in his bed, and cried out with fright. The dream was broken. His attendants came running to him, and he sent them for his sages. To the sages he cried, " Tell me the meaning of this dream! " And he told his dream to them, but they could not understand it. Then he called for the Book of the King, and there he read what his father had written: " Beware of the Bull and the Ram, for by the Bull and the Ram the seed of the king will be cut off."

When he read these words, the king's heart began to knock like the hand of death, and sweat was upon his forehead. He called the queen and told her of his dream and of its meaning. The queen was frightened, and their children were terribly frightened.

Then the king reflected, " How can I be harmed by a bull or a ram, when there is not one in all the kingdom? " And his heart was more quiet, but still he was afraid, so he called the wisest of the sages to him and asked, " How may I be sure? "

The aged seer answered, " I have a remedy for

fear that was told me by my father. The sun has three hundred and sixty-five beams, and there is one place where the light of all three hundred and sixty-five beams come together, and upon that spot grows an iron rod. Whoever has fear needs but go there and touch that rod, and his fear will be taken from him."

The king was pleased with this advice, and he called his wife, and they took their children and all their family, and they said to the seer, " Guide us to that place where the three hundred and sixty-five rays of the sun come together."

Then the seer led the way, and the king and all his family followed, and they went a great distance until they came to a parting of the roads. And there an angel stood. He was the Angel of Wrath, for of every human act of rage an angel is born, twisted, and meagre, and hard, and the commander of all the angels born of anger was that Angel of Wrath who stood in the road before them. His form was powerful, and his eyes were cold blue fire, and a flaming sword was in his hand.

Of him, they asked the way.

For there were four roads. There was a smooth highway, and there was a road of quagmires seething with reptiles and vile worms; and there was a road that broke into bottomless gaps and craggy holes jagged with sharp stones: there men fell, and were swallowed up; and there was a road that became a flaming fire.

The Angel of Wrath pointed his sword, and it was to the road that became a flaming fire.

The seer knew, for his father had given him an omen; but the king did not know.

And as they went, the seer watched for signs of the flames before them. After they had gone a long way, he saw the fire, and he looked and saw in the midst of the fire a sea of molten red, clear as crystal blood, and safely over the fiery sea there went a row of angelic beings wearing kingly mantles and crowns, and with them went a row of aged Jews, each wrapped in his praying-shawl, with his holy phylacteries wound upon his arms and forehead.

Then the seer said to the king, " The road is a flaming fire. I have an omen from my father, that whoever goes nearer than four leagues to that fire will be burned to death, and so I will not go further."

But the king looked into the fire, and saw the row of regal beings wearing golden crowns, and he said, " See, a king may pass safely through the flames! "

Then the king led all his family, and they went into the fire, and were burned, and the king and all his seed were entirely consumed.

The sage turned back, and came once more to the palace. There all the wise men were assembled, and they wondered how it could be that the seer had come home unharmed, while the king and all his family were dead. " Was it not written," they said, " that only a bull and a ram might destroy the seed of the king? And the king took care that there might be not one bull or ram in all his land! Then through what power was he killed, with all his royal family? "

The aged Jew cried out to them, " It is through me that the king and all his family met death! The seers truly saw his death in the stars, but did not understand what they saw. For the phylacteries are made of the hide of the bull, and the fringes that hang on the praying-shawl are woven of the wool of the ram. And so the bull and the ram, called down by my prayers to curse him, brought the end to his seed on earth. For in that row of kings whom he saw going safely through the flames were only those rulers in whose lands Jews might live unharmed, and freely worship their God in praying-shawl and holy phylacteries. And he thought to pass safely through the flames with them, but he could not take his place among them! "

THE PRINCE

THERE was a king who had no children, and he was greatly troubled with thought that after his death his kingdom would pass into the hands of strangers. So he called to him all the physicians and all the magicians of his realm, and commanded them to make use of their learning and of their magic, that a prince might be born to the royal family. But they were of no help to him.

At last in despair he turned upon the Jews who lived in his kingdom, for, he said, " I have heard that among the Jews there are secret saints whose prayers can bring whatever is in the heavens down on earth." So he commanded the Jews to bring one of these saints to the palace.

In each generation there are thirty-six men whose virtue bears up the world; they live unknown among other men, and they are called hidden Tsadikim. When the king commanded that one of them be brought to the palace, the Jews did not know where to turn, but one man went up to another, asking, " Might you be one of the secret Tsadikim? "

There was a shoe-maker in a village; he lived quietly, earning bread for himself and his family, working each day, but resting on Sabbath. Then all the people in the village bethought themselves that they had never known him to do any wrong, and they said to one another, " He must be a secret Tsadik! " But when they came to him and asked him, he only said, " I don't know anything about it. I am a shoe-maker." Still, the word went from one village to another, and

THE PRINCE

at last it came to the king that in a certain village there lived a shoe-maker who was really a hidden Tsadik, but who said he knew nothing about it.

The king commanded that the man be brought before him, and when the Tsadik stood in the palace, the king spoke to him in a friendly way, saying, " You know that all your people are in my power, and I can do good or ill to them as I please. Therefore I ask you in a friendly way to pray that my queen may have a child."

The Tsadik went into a little room and spoke to God. Then he returned to the king. " Within a year," the Tsadik said, " a child will be born to the queen." And he went home to his village, and made shoes.

Before the year had passed, the queen gave birth to a daughter. The little girl was so beautiful that whoever looked once upon her never ceased wondering at her loveliness; and she was so clever that when she was four years old she could play music upon many instruments, and speak all the languages of mankind. Emperors and sages came from distant lands to look upon and speak with the child.

At first the king was happy with his daughter, but then he grew discontented, for he wanted a son to rule after him, in order that his kingdom might not fall into strange hands. So he commanded that the secret Tsadik should again be brought before him.

But when the king's messenger went to seek out the Tsadik, he was told that the man had died.

The king said, " Let the Jews find another Tsadik! " So the Jews asked of one another, and sought amongst themselves, until they found another of the thirty-six secret Tsadikim, and they told the king where he was, and the king sent for him and said to him in a friendly way, " If you do not help me, remember that your people are in my power."

Then the Tsadik answered, " I will help you, if you will give me what I ask."

" I will give half of my possessions for a son! " the king cried.

" Then," said the Tsadik, " you must bring me precious stones, for in every jewel there is a quality of good, and the secret virtues of the jewels are written in the angel's book. Bring me every kind of precious stone, for I have need of them all."

The king commanded that jewels be brought. And from all parts of the world there were brought to him the largest and purest of precious stones: a diamond as radiant as a falling star, a pearl as white as an infant's smile, a ruby deep as a friendly eye, and sapphire, agate, carbuncle, and opal stones. These the king gave to the Tsadik who took them and crushed them into a powder; the powder he poured into a goblet of wine. Then he gave half of the wine to the king to drink, and the queen drank the other half.

" You will have a son," said the Tsadik, " who will be made entirely of precious stones, and who will have all the virtues of all the jewels in the world." Then he went home.

A son was born to the queen.

Now the king was completely happy, for he had a son to reign after him. And though the child appeared to be made like all other children, and not made of precious stones as the Tsadik had predicted, the king was satisfied, for the boy was even more beautiful than his sister, and he too was able to speak all the languages of mankind when he was four years old, and he knew besides all the wisdom of the world, so that rulers came from far places to ask advice of him.

But when the little girl saw the emperors and sages coming to court to seek her younger brother, and no longer for her sake, and when she heard the beauty and the wisdom of her brother constantly praised, while she was forgotten, she became jealous of her brother. Only one thing pleased her. " They said he would be made entirely of precious stones," she remembered, " but he is made like all of us."

One day as he was carving wood with a sharp knife, the prince cut his finger. His sister ran to bind up his finger, but as she looked into the wound she saw a gleaming sapphire there.

Then her jealousy turned to hatred, and she thought only of how she could be revenged upon her brother.

There was consternation in the palace because of the prince's injury, and when the princess saw how the king was troubled, and the people anxious, and the servants ran everywhere, she thought, " I too will be ill, and then they will remember me! " So she pretended to be sick.

Physicians were sent to her, but they could not find out the cause of her illness; at last the magicians were called, but none of the magicians could help her. She lay in her bed, and thought with hatred of her brother, and how he was indeed made of precious stones, and her jealousy gave her no rest. Then the sorcerer who was the most cunning of all the king's magicians came to the little girl, and as soon as he saw her he said, " You are not ill, but are only pretending illness!" She looked into his wicked eyes, and they were like two hard stones pressing upon her. Then she told the sorcerer the truth.

"I am not ill," she said, "but I cannot bear my brother's beauty; he is so beautiful that no one any longer remembers me." Then the princess begged the wizard, "Tell me," she cried, "is there no way to bewitch a person, so that all his body will become covered with itching sores?"

"There is a way," the wizard said. "I can make a charm against him."

But the clever little princess thought, "What if another magician should come, and break your charm? Then my brother will be beautiful again."

"If the charm is buried in water," the sorcerer replied, "it can never again be broken."

So they made an evil charm against the prince, and they bound their sorcery in a silken cloth and threw it into a deep pool where it could never again be found.

Then the prince's tender skin became red, and broke; sores appeared on his face and hands, and there were itching and leprous sores all over his body.

The king was terrified, the entire kingdom was in mourning because of the loathsome disease that had come upon the beautiful prince. Every physician and every sage hurried to the palace to try to heal the suffering boy. They covered him with balm and with ointments, but the sores remained upon him, and he tore at his loathsome skin.

The physicians said, "He cannot be cured."

Then the king cried, "It is the Jews who have brought this thing upon me!" and he commanded that the Jews cause the boy to be healed of his sores.

Once more the Jews sought amongst themselves for a secret Tsadik. And they found that Tsadik who had brought about the birth of the prince, and he was brought again to the palace.

" See what you have done! " the king cried. " You promised me a son who would be made entirely of precious stones, and instead he is covered with sores."

" Let me go into a little room where I may be alone," said the Tsadik. Then he went into a tiny chamber, and closed the door, and stood alone and spoke to God.

" It was not to bring glory upon myself that I did this thing," said the Tsadik, " but it was for the glory of your Name that I said that a child would be born, all made of precious stones. And now, see how my words have been fulfilled; the boy is covered with sores."

Then the truth was revealed to the Tsadik, for he knew that nothing happened without reason, and that the depths of loathsome sin must be felt before the heights of purest beauty may be known. And he came out and said to the king, " A sorcerer has made a charm against the prince, to cover him with evil. The charm has been buried in water, so that it may not be destroyed."

The king was terrified, for he thought that the prince would never be well again. " Is there nothing that can be done? " he begged. " Is there no magician more powerful than the evil one who has done this thing? "

" Since the charm has been buried in water," the Tsadik said, " there is only one way in which it can be broken. The magician who made the charm must be found, and he also must be thrown into the water."

"Take all the magicians of my kingdom," cried the king, "and throw them into the sea! If only my son will be well!"

Then he issued a decree that on the very next day every wizard, sorcerer, and magician in his realm should be thrown into the water.

When the princess heard this decree, her guilt made her afraid, for she thought, "Now the charm will be found out, and they will know that I have done this thing to my brother." So she ran to the pond, to take the charm out of the water before anyone else would find it there. But as the Princess leaned far over the pond seeking for the evil charm, she fell into the water herself, and she sank to the bottom of the deep pool.

Then the servants hurried through the palace crying, "The princess has fallen into the pool!" and there was crying and wailing everywhere.

But when the Tsadik heard them he only smiled and said, "Now the prince will be well."

And so it was as he said. The sores upon the body of the prince began to close, and to dry up, and to fall away. And as the wounds fell away, the sickly skin became dry and hard, and it slipped from him as a cloud from the face of the sun; then the prince stood healed and shining before them, and their eyes were scarcely strong enough to look upon the dazzling brilliance of the boy, for now anyone might see that the prince was indeed made entirely of precious stones.

And he had all the virtues of all the jewels in the world.

THE SPIDER AND THE FLY

PERHAPS you think I will tell you everything, so that you may be able to understand my story. I will begin to tell the story.

There was a king who fought a great battle against many nations, and won the battle, and took thousands of prisoners from among all the nations. Every year, on the day of his victory, he caused a great feast to be made; and to the conqueror's festival there came princes and emperors from all the kingdoms of the world. He would have clowns at his festival, to entertain him and his guests with imitations of the different peoples of the world. The comedians would dress themselves in long cloaks, with scarves over their heads, as Arabs of the desert; and then they would appear as Turks, and as Spaniards, and they would make themselves fat as Germans, and they would make fun of whomever they pleased; and naturally they did not forget to put on long beards and to scratch themselves like Jews.

The king sat and watched the clowns, and tried to guess when they were Arabs, or Germans, or Spaniards, or Jews. Then he ordered that the Book of Nations be brought to him, and he looked in the Book of Nations to see how well the clowns had portrayed the different peoples. For the comedians, too, had looked in that book.

But while the king sat over the open volume, he noticed a spider that crept along the edge of the page; then he saw that a fly stood upon the open page. With its thin hair-like legs the spider pulled itself up the side of the book, then it reached its legs slowly over the side of the book, trying to crawl onto the page where the fly stood.

Just then a wind came and blew on the page so that it stood erect, and the spider could not reach the fly. Then the spider turned away, and for a while it crept along the table, as if it had forgotten the fly. Slowly and carefully it put out its feet, and then it stood still for a moment, as if it were waiting to hear a sound.

When the wind was gone, the page fell back to its place; then the spider turned and crept in a circle, coming nearer and nearer again to the edge of the book, until it clambered up the sides of the pages, and its little specks of eyes peered over the cliff-like top of the book onto the wide plain where the fly remained standing. And the spider lifted its claw onto the page.

Once more the wind came, and blew the page upward, and the spider fell away from the edge, and could not reach the fly. This happened several times, but at last the wind was quiet for a long while, and the spider returned to the book, and crept up the side, and placed its feet upon the open page, and drew its body up onto the page. In that instant, the wind blew hard, and turned the page over entirely upon the spider, so that he lay on his back between the pages of the book.

He tried to crawl out, but he could only crawl a little way, and he could not turn himself aright, and though he moved with all his strength he could only go a little further into the darkness that pressed upon him between the pages of the book; and there he remained, until nothing remained of him.

As for the fly, I will not tell you what he did.

But the king saw all that had happened, and he knew that what he saw was not a simple thing, but that there was a meaning intended for him in what he had seen; and it was as though he heard a message vaguely through thick walls. Then he fell into deep thought, trying to understand what had happened before his eyes; the guests at the festival saw the king was lost in thought, and did not disturb him.

For a long while the king leaned over the book, wondering, but he could not find a meaning to what he had seen; at last he became very tired, and his head leaned further over the page until it lay upon his spread arms, and he slept. Then he dreamed.

He dreamed that he sat upon his throne in his palace, and over him hung his portrait, and according to the custom in the palaces of kings, his crown hung over his portrait. He sat there, holding a precious image in his hands. Suddenly, hosts of people began to pour out of the image. He threw the thing away from him.

Then the sleeping king saw how the people that rushed out of the image turned, and climbed above him, and cut his head from his portrait. They seized his crown and hurled it into the mud. Then they ran toward him with their knives drawn, to kill him.

In that instant, a page out of the book upon which he slept stood erect and shielded him, so that the oncoming horde could do him no harm; when they had turned away, the page fell back into its place in the book.

Once more the angry people rushed to kill him, and the page stood before him and shielded him so that they had to turn back. Seven times they rushed upon him, and seven times they were prevented from harming him.

Then the king in his sleep was eager to see what was written on the leaf that had so well protected him, and what nation out of the Book of Nations might be represented there. But as he was about to look at the page, he was overcome by a terrible fear; the edges of his hair felt like ice. He began to scream.

The princes and the emperors who were his guests heard the king screaming in his sleep, and wanted to shake him that he might awake out of his frightful dream, but it was forbidden to touch the king while he slept. Then they began to shout, and to beat upon drums, and to make wild noises that might awaken the king, but he did not hear them, and only trembled, and cried out, and shouted with fear as he slept over the Book of Nations.

Then a high mountain came to him and said, " Why are you screaming so? I was asleep for many ages, and nothing could awaken me, but your screams have broken my sleep! "

" How can I keep from screaming? " cried the king. " See how all the people are assembled, how they come against me with their drawn knives! They will kill me! And I have nothing to protect me but this little sheet of paper! "

" As long as it stands before you, you have nothing to fear," said the mountain. " I too have many enemies, but that same leaf has protected me, and I am not afraid. Come, and I'll show you my enemies."

They went, and the king saw myriad upon myriad of warriors assembled at the foot of the mountain;

they were shouting and dancing and loudly blowing their trumpets.

" Why do they sing so gayly, and why do they dance so triumphantly? " the king asked of the mountain.

" Each time one of them thinks of a plan by which they may come up on me, they become wild with joy, and hold a feast, and they dance and sing in triumph," said the mountain. " But the same page protects me by what is written upon it, just as you are protected."

Then the king saw that a tablet stood on the top of the mountain, but because the mountain was very high, he could not read what was written on the tablet.

Behind them, however, was another stone on which this was written: " He that has all his teeth may come up to the top of the mountain."

The king thought, " Surely there are many people who can easily go up this way." But he looked on the ground and saw that they were not pebbles, but teeth of men and beasts upon which he trod, and all over the side of the mountain there were little mounds of teeth.

For the Power of the Name had caused a grass to grow on the sides of that mountain, and this grass was such that it drew out the teeth of all those who passed over it. The enemies from below tried to ride over it on the backs of swift horses, or in wagons, thinking that thus they would not touch the grass, nevertheless their teeth fell from them, and they could go no further up against the mountain.

When the king had seen this, he returned to the place of his own dream, and saw that now his own enemies, who were the people that had rushed out of the image, took up the head of his portrait and placed it back upon the shoulders; then they took the crown out of the mud, and washed it, and hung it in its accustomed place.

And then the king awoke.

At once he looked into the book, to see what was written on the page that had protected him. And he found that that page in the Book of Nations was the page of the Jews. He read carefully what was written there, and he began to understand the truth, and he said, " I will become a Jew."

But when he had become a Jew he was not yet satisfied, and cried, " The whole world must know the truth, and I will make all the peoples in the world into Jews."

But he could not think of a way by which he could show the truth to the whole world, and cause all men to become Jews, so he decided, " I will go and seek a sage who can tell me the meaning of everything in my dream, and then I shall know how to do what I want to do."

The king disguised himself as a simple traveller, and took two companions, and went out to seek a wise man.

Wherever he went he asked, " Is there anyone here who can explain a dream? " Though he travelled all over the earth, he could find no one who understood the meaning of his dream. But at last he was told of a sage who lived in a place that had no name.

When the king had been to every place that had a name, he continued to seek, and at last he reached a place where there were no hills or trees or rivers, no houses, and no beasts; and there was a man.

" What is the name of this place? " the king asked.

And the man answered him, " This place has no name." Then the king knew that he had come to the end of his journey, and that this man was the sage who could tell him the meaning of his dream. So he told the wise man the truth about himself. " I am no simple traveller," he said, " but a king who has won many battles and conquered many nations; and now I would like to know the true meaning of my dream."

The sage answered that he could not give him the meaning of his dream, but that if the king would wait until a day that was not in a month, he might himself learn what he wanted to know. " For on that day," the wise man said, " I gather the seeds of all things and make them into a perfume. And when the perfume is spread all about you, you will have the power to see for yourself all that you desire to know."

The king said, " I will wait."

He waited. And there came a time when he no longer knew the day and the month. Then the wizard brought him a perfume, and burned the perfume until it rose all about the king. And in the cloud the king began to see.

He saw himself as he had been even before he had become himself; he saw his soul as it waited in readiness before coming down to this world, and he saw his soul being led through all the worlds above and below, while a voice cried, " If there is anyone who has evil to say of this soul, let him speak! " But the soul passed through all the regions, and not one voice was raised against it. Then the king saw his soul in readiness to go down and live upon earth. But at that instant someone came hurrying, running, crying, " Hear me, God! If this soul goes down on earth, what will there remain for me to do? Why was I created! "

The king looked, to see who it was that cried out so against his soul's going down to earth, and he saw that it was the Evil One himself!

And the Evil One was answered: " This soul must go down on earth. As for you, you must think of something to do." Upon this, the Evil One went away.

Then the king saw his soul being led through the high regions, from one heaven to another, until at last it stood before the Court of highest heaven, ready to take its oath to go down and live on earth. And still the Evil One had not returned. Before the soul was given oath, a messenger was sent to bring the Evil One before the Throne. The Evil One came, and brought with him a wizen old man whom he had known for a very long time. And as he came up with the bent old man, he was laughing, and chuckling, and smiling to himself, and he said, " I've thought of a way out of it all! You can let this soul go down on earth! "

Then the king saw his soul go down on earth, and he saw himself born, and he saw everything that had happened to him on earth, he saw how he had become king, and how he had gone out in battles, and slaughtered peoples, and won victories, and taken prisoners.

He saw that among the myriads of prisoners he had taken there was a beautiful maiden. The maiden possessed every loveliness that was to be found on earth, the beauty of form that was felt as sweet water under the fingers, the beauty of the eyes that was as a caress of the hands, and the beauty that is heard like the sound of bells touched by the wind. But when the king looked upon her, he saw that her beauty was not her own, but that it came forth like a perfume out of the tiny image that she wore upon herself. And it was this image that contained all forms of beauty, and because it was upon her, it seemed that all those forms of beauty were her own.

And only the very good and the very wise can go higher upon this mountain, for no more may be told.

THE RABBI'S SON

NOT long ago there lived a rabbi who in all his life had scarcely lifted his head from the study of the holy books, and who was so strict in his observance of every last dot in the ritual that he would scarcely raise his eyes to heaven without first seeking a law that might tell him whether it was permitted at that moment and hour to raise one's eyes to heaven. And in all the world there was nothing that angered him so much as the practices of those who were called Chassidim, for in their wild prayer, in their miracles of healing, and in their carelessness of the strictures of the law, he saw the hand of the evil one. And when he found men in his own village going over to the ways of the Chassidim, the rabbi became bitter against them, and he fought with all his strength to prevent another soul from being lost to the erring ones, and he thought, "After I am dead, there will be none to prevent them, and they will all go and become followers of the mad, howling tsadikim, who disgrace the Sabbath with their loud singing and lusty dancing, and who scarcely know how to read in the holy books." The rabbi longed for a son who would continue after him to keep the people to the observance of the holy law.

When a son was born to him in his old age, he took it joyfully as a sign from above that his way was the only path to heaven, and that the way would not be left without a guide. The rabbi thought, " My son will be a great light against the chassidim; he will destroy them entirely, with their ignorant tsadikim, their mad chanting in the woods, and their magic tricks of healing." He was watchful over the boy every instant of day and night, that the child might not touch even the shadow of an impurity.

The youth that grew was remarkable in learning. He sat on a high stool near the table, and studied the books that were before him. But as the young boy sat on the stool, he would sometimes lift his eyes from the pages of the holy books, and his gaze would reach through the window out into the fields, into the distance that was yellow and green with leaves; then his soul would glide forth upon the path of his gaze, and his soul would hover like a bird in the free air.

At those moments the boy felt himself drawn as toward a singing voice, and he was very happy. But then he would remember his books, and force his eyes back upon the page, and hold his head down with both his hands, that he might not err.

More often the longing came upon him, and his soul went out to the call of a song, as a bird answering the song of its mate. And in that time the boy was alight with a holiness that made bright the entire room, and joy was all about him. But when he returned to his books he felt himself dragged down to listen to the mouths of the dead, and there was a yearning and a longing in him for he knew not what.

The flame and the yearning consumed him, his body became weak, and he was as a trembling candle-flame that may die with every puff of the wind. Still he did not know what he desired, but his yearning was as that of the unborn souls that await their embodiment on earth.

The rabbi saw that his son was becoming weak, and

CHEDER

he spoke with him of all the wonders of the law's myriad commands, and of his life that was needed to combat the Chassidim on earth. But in all the things that the rabbi said, there was no help for the boy; only when his father spoke of the evil of the Chassidim, only then he felt a trembling within him, and a sudden warmth.

Among the young scholars with whom he sometimes studied, there were two who went secretly among the Chassidim; and when they saw the rabbi's son become so pale, and losing his heart for learning, they said, " What is it that is ill with you? "

He told them, " I feel a longing for something, and I cannot tell what it is."

Then they said to him, " Only one man can help you, and he is the great Tsadik who lives one day's journey from here. You must go to him, for he has the power to release your soul to its destiny."

" Is he pure? " asked the rabbi's son.

" We do not know whether he is pure," they told him, " for he does not keep himself from contact with the sinful. But we do know that he never leaves any one until he has taken his burden from him."

" Is he learned? " asked the rabbi's son.

" We do not know whether he is learned," they answered, " for he lives in a hut in the forest, and works as a wood-cutter. But he knows the song that the sparrow sings to heaven."

Then the boy went to his father the rabbi and said, " Let me go to see a Tsadik who lives in a little town a day away."

The rabbi was deeply pained at his son's words, for he knew that the Tsadik was but a simple man, a leader of the Chassidim. " What help can he be to you, my son," the rabbi asked, " when you yourself have more learning than he? "

The boy returned to his studies, but again he felt the terrible longing come over his soul and his eyes lifted, and he looked into the distance. Then he went to his father and begged him, " Let me go."

The rabbi saw his son become more frail and wan each day, until when the boy asked him a third time, the rabbi said, " You may not go alone to him, for it may be the evil one who is drawing you on this way. But I will go with you to this ignorant man, that you may see him and forget him."

When they had put the horses to the cart, the rabbi said, " Let us see whether there will be a sign from heaven upon this journey. If nothing happens to delay the journey, it is a sign that this is a true pilgrimage; but if we should be stopped on our way, it is a sign that we must turn back, and we will return."

So they rode forth, and all went well until they came to a shallow brook, but as the cart was crossing the brook, one of the horses slipped and fell and overturned the cart, so that the rabbi and his son were thrown into the water.

When they had come out of the water, and righted the cart, the rabbi said: " You see, my son, heaven has sent us a sign to turn back, for this is an evil journey." So they returned home, and the boy sat again over his books. But soon the heaviness returned to his heart, and he felt the call of the distance. He feared to speak to his father, for he remembered the omen on their journey. Days passed, and each day the boy became weaker, until he was as a dying man who no longer fears what may be said on earth. "Father," he cried, "I must go and speak with the Tsadik!"

Once more the rabbi consented, and they rode on their way. But when they had ridden two-thirds of a day, the cart went over a great stone, and both axles of the cart were broken.

"This Tsadik must surely be an impostor," the rabbi declared, "for we have had another omen, and our journey to him is barred." They mended the wagon, and returned home.

But the boy's soul was more than ever unquiet, until he prevailed upon the rabbi to set out for a third time upon the journey. "But father," he begged, "let us not take what may befall by chance as an omen from heaven. If the horse slips, or the wagon breaks, have we proof that the Tsadik is sinful?"

The rabbi said, "But if there is a sign of sin against him alone, will you obey?"

"I will obey, and return home, and never ask to go to him again."

They set out on their third journey. All went well; at night they came to an inn not far from the village of the Tsadik. As they sat over their evening meal, the boy dreamy and lost in awaited happiness, the rabbi began to speak with a merchant who sat at a near-by table.

"Where does a rabbi travel?" the merchant enquired.

"On his way," said the rabbi, for he was ashamed to say that he was going to consult a man of no learning. "And you?" he asked.

" I am a merchant; I have just been to a village," said the stranger. And he spoke the name of the Tsadik's place.

Then, as one who remembers the sounds of a name, the rabbi said: " I have heard that many people come to consult with a wonder-worker who lives in that same village."

At this, the merchant laughed out loud. " Don't speak of him! " he shouted. " I have just come from that very man's house! "

The boy raised his head, as one who listens in a dream, and his wide eyes pierced the stranger.

" Is it indeed true," the rabbi asked, " that he is a holy man? "

" A holy man! " the stranger laughed. " He is an impostor and an agent of the evil one! I myself saw him defile the Sabbath! "

Then the rabbi turned to his son and said, " You have heard what the stranger has told us, in all innocence, not knowing where we were bound."

" I have heard," the boy replied, and his voice was as the voice of the dead.

They returned home.

Soon after, the boy died.

One night, as the grieving rabbi slept, his son appeared to him in a dream; the youth was wrapped in anger, and as the rabbi asked him, " My son, why are you angry? " the boy cried, " Go to that Tsadik to whom I longed to go! " The rabbi awoke, and remembered his dream, and said to himself, " Perhaps it was a chance dream," and did not go.

But again his son appeared to him as he slept, and the boy wore the form of the Angel of Wrath. And he cried, " Go to the Tsadik! Go! " This time the rabbi thought, " The dream is the work of the evil one." But when his son appeared to him a third time, the rabbi knew that he must go.

And as he came to that same inn where he had stopped with his son, he entered, to pass the night. He sat alone in the room, and did not touch the food that was placed before him; his heart was heavy. Then a voice spoke, a voice of laughter, saying, " Ah, the rabbi is here again."

The rabbi looked up, and saw the same merchant whom he had met that other night when he had stopped at the inn.

" The rabbi is here again," the merchant said, " and this time he is alone! "

" Are you not that merchant whom I met here once before? " the rabbi asked.

" Indeed I am! " said the stranger, and laughing he opened wide his mouth and cried, " If you like, I'll swallow you alive."

The rabbi started with fright. " Who are you! " he murmured, trembling.

" Do you remember," the stranger said, " how you and your son once rode to see the Tsadik, and on the way your horse tripped and fell in the brook? Yet your son made you go again on the way to that holy man, but the second time the axles of your wagon were broken? And the third time you met me here, and I told you that the man was not holy, but an impostor who sinned on Sabbath? Then you turned back once more, and so your son died of loneliness and grief? Go, rabbi! now that I have got rid of your son you may go on your way to the Chassid; for know that in your son there lived the power of the lesser flame, and the power of the greater flame was in the Tsadik, and if they two had come together on this earth, Messiah would have descended! But I placed obstacles in your way, until your son was dead; and now, rabbi, you can go to see the Tsadik! "

With these words, the stranger vanished.

And the rabbi continued on his journey, and came to the hut of the Chassid. And there he wept, " Alas, for him who is lost unto us, and cannot be found again! "

THE SAGE AND THE SIMPLETON

WHO WAS NOT SO FOOLISH AS HE SEEMED

IN a hamlet in the provinces there lived two wealthy men, each of whom had a son. One of the children was so clever that he could make the sun believe it shone at night; the other boy was a simpleton, he was no fool, but he had only a little common sense, and could talk only of plain things as they were. Even though they were of such different natures, the children liked each other, and were fast friends.

Misfortune overtook the two wealthy men, and they began to lose their money; with each loss they became more desperate in their commerce, trying to win back what they had lost, until they had nothing left at all except the houses in which they lived.

Then the fathers said to the boys, " You will have to find a way to earn a living."

So the simpleton went and became a shoe-maker's apprentice, and learned how to make shoes.

But the clever boy would not set himself to so humble a task. " I'll look around the world a bit," he thought, "and see what I can do." He went to the market-place; and just then a handsome carriage drawn by four swift narrow-headed horses whirled into the square and halted. Two merchants got out of the carriage to refresh themselves at the inn. The clever boy at once went up to them and asked, " Where are you going? "

" To Warsaw," they told him.

" Take me with you, I'll be your servant on the road," he said.

The merchants saw that he was a clever and eager boy, so they took him to be their servant.

But when they had come to Warsaw he thought, "I'll look around; perhaps I can find some better thing to do." He went to the market-place and began to talk with a young man who stood near a stall. First, the clever boy asked about the merchants who had brought him to Warsaw.

"Oh, they are good honest people," the young man said, "but their trade keeps them always on the roads."

The clever young man thought he would rather stay in one place and learn a craft, so he went to his masters and said he could serve them no longer.

In the market-place he had noticed the elegant caps and fine curved shoes of the silk merchants, and he thought, "I would like to be one of them." So he went to a silk merchants' shop and asked if a helper was needed.

He began to work there, but it was the custom for a beginner to work as an under-helper, and the under-helpers had to do hard work, carrying heavy bolts of cloth in their arms and on their backs through the streets all day, and sometimes up many flights of stairs. This was not to his taste.

And though his cleverness and quickness of mind had already been observed by his masters, and they were eager to have him remain with them, he thought: "What future is there for me here? I may earn a living, and marry. There is plenty of time for that. First, I'll see if there is a better place for me in the world." So he became a servant to some merchants who were going to London. And from London he went to Paris, and he went to Germany, and Spain. Thus he travelled about for several years, until he was no longer a youth, but a grown man, much wiser and cleverer than ever before.

He thought, " It's time I learned a craft, and settled down." Of all the crafts he had seen, the work of a goldsmith pleased him most, for it dealt in riches, and required great skill.

So he went to Italy, and became a goldsmith. As he was quick to learn, he did not have to remain an apprentice for several years, but became a master goldsmith in three months; and then he became so clever at spinning slender threads of gold into mysterious and intricate patterns, into images of birds whose every feather might be counted, and of trees whose every leaf might be seen, that he was soon famous as a greater artisan than the master who had taught him, and at last he was master of all the masters of his craft. But still he was not content.

" Today there is a fashion for delicate ornaments of gold," he thought, " but tomorrow the fashion may change, and there will be no work for the goldsmith." So he went to Amsterdam, and learned the craft of cutting and setting jewels. This, too, he was able to do in a few months; he became a master jeweller. But still he was not content.

" I will learn a craft that cannot pass from fashion," he thought. " I will learn to do something that is always needed, and that will employ the wisdom of my mind as well as the cunning of my eyes and hands." So he went to Paris, studied medicine, and became a physician.

In a short time he had become a skilful physician

and a learned philosopher; then all the world seemed stale to him, and everything in the world seemed but a trifle; he could do anything, and nothing seemed worth doing; he could have anything, and nothing seemed worth having.

Of all the people whom he met, none were clever enough to talk with him, for beside his skill, and his mastery of so many crafts, and his philosophy, and his knowledge of medicine, he found all other men simple. Then he became weary of going about in the world, and he thought, " I will marry, and live quietly in my own house."

When he had decided to take a wife, he sought in all the courts of brilliance, but could find no woman who pleased him, for all their talk seemed foolish, and he was tired of listening.

Then one day a new plan came into his mind. " I will return to the town of my birth," he thought. " They will see what a great man I have become though I left the village as a poor boy. And there, among them, I will live in honour and in peace."

Meanwhile the simpleton had become a cobbler. And since he was a simpleton, he had to remain an apprentice for many years, and even then he never quite learned how to make shoes; but he set himself up as a cobbler, and took a wife. It was very difficult for him to earn his scant living, for he was not a quick or clever workman. He had to labour so long over each shoe that there was scarcely time for him to eat; but when he had pushed the needle into the leather, and pulled through the thread, he would seize a bit of bread, and eat. Nevertheless he was a cheerful per-

son, always merry, and though he was poor he be-
haved as though he had every good thing in the world
to eat, and the best of wines to drink, and the costliest of garments to wear.

As he pulled through his thread he would sing out,
" My wife, let us have dinner! Bring in the lentil
soup! " She would give him a piece of dry bread, and
he would eat it and say, " Ah! The soup tastes wonderful today! Now let's have the roast goose! " His
wife would give him another crust of bread, and he
would eat it, and smack his lips and cry, " What a
marvellous goose! What a wonderful cook you are,
my beloved! Now give me my mug of beer! " She
would give him a glass of water, and he would drain it
down at a gulp, and wipe his lips with his hand, and
his eyes would dance, and he would say, " Now let
us have cakes and wine! " So she would give him
another bit of dry bread and another glass of water,
and he would drink the water as though it were wine
out of the king's cellar. The truth was, that the simpleton really tasted fine lentil soup, and fish broiled
in fat, and roast goose, and all manner of cakes and
fruit in the dry bread that was given him; and the
water he drank was like beer and brandy and wine to
his lips.

And so it was with his clothes. He and his wife had
but one cloak for both of them: a ragged, bedraggled
old sheepskin. When he had to go to market he
would sing out, " Sweet wife, give me my fur over-
coat." Then she would give him the old sheepskin,
and he would put it on his back, and turn one way
and the other saying, " What a marvellous fur coat!
The rich will die of envy! " And so he would go to

the market. If he had to go among fine folk, as to a funeral, he would say, " Dear wife, bring me my frock coat! " Then she would hand him the ragged cloak, and he would put it on, and cluck his tongue and say, " What an elegant frock coat! " And off he would go to the fashionable funeral. And when he had to wear a long coat to the synagogue, he would ask for his fine long coat, and she would bring him the sheepskin cloak, and he would put it on, and marvel at its length and beauty.

He was always lively and cheerful over his work, and whenever he had at last clumsily managed to finish a shoe, he would hold it up and gaze upon it, and shower praise upon it; even if the toe were where the heel should be, he would cry out, " What a wonderful work of art! What a beautiful shoe! A sweet shoe! A perfect shoe! A marvel of a shoe! See, wife, what a piece of craft it is! What a jewel of a little shoe it is! "

Then she would say, " If your shoes are so wonderful, how is it that the other cobblers receive three gulden for a pair of shoes, while you get only a gulden and a half? "

" What have I to do with them? " he would retort. " That's their business, and this is my business. Let us better find out how much profit I have made on this shoe! " Then he would say, " Leather cost me so much, and thread so much, and nails so much and so much," and he would add on his fingers, and cry, " Why, I've earned ten pence profit on this shoe! " And he was happy and content, though everyone made a joke of him.

The townspeople would come into his shop just to

make fun of him; they would tell him all sorts of tales, for he was ready to believe anything. When they began to tell him something he would say, " But — no fooling? " And they would answer solemnly, " No fooling." Then he would listen and believe, even if they told him that a fence-post had given forth milk.

And in the end, if he saw that they had indeed made fun of him, he would say, " Well, everyone knows I am a simpleton. What good does it do you to prove yourself cleverer than I am? I'm so great a fool that you might be much wiser than I am, and still be fool enough."

Then one day they came to him and said, " Do you know, your clever friend is coming home! "

The simpleton cried, " Really? No fooling? " And when they said, " No fooling! " he called to his wife, " Bring me my finest fur coat! " She brought him the old cloak, and he put it on, and ran out on the road to meet the friend of his youth.

The celebrated physician was indeed coming along the road in a great carriage, and when he saw the simpleton running toward him, the ragged cloak streaming in the wind, he thought, " The man surely is mad." But the simpleton greeted the sage with joy, crying, " Praised be God for bringing you home, and letting me live to see you once more! Beloved brother! " Then the philosopher, to whom all mankind was as dust, and all the world as offal, was indeed touched by the friendliness of the simpleton, and he took him up in his carriage and rode into the town with him.

During the years of his absence, the wise man's father had died, and his house had fallen to pieces for lack of care, so that now the philosopher had no home. He went to the best hostelry in the village, but it was scarcely good enough for him, and he was troubled by the noise of many people, and the food did not please him, and he lived in constant torment. His simple friend came to him every day asking if there were not some comfort he could bring him. And when the cobbler heard his friend complain so much of his quarters, he said, " Come to my house! I will give you the best room, and my wife will take care of your comfort, and you will be able to live as you choose."

The philosopher thought, " Perhaps it will be well." And he said he would go.

Then the simpleton ran home and called his wife, and they cleaned the best room in the house, and put all of their furniture into it, and spent their last copper so that the room might be as fine as they could manage. And the philosopher came to live there.

Meanwhile his fame had begun to spread through the kingdom; it was said that he was a marvellous goldsmith, and unequalled as a cutter of precious stones, and that his skill as a physician was miraculous. And people began to come to him, to test his skill.

A neighbouring baron brought gold and asked him to make a gold ring. The sage set to work and wove a delicate ring of the precious metal, carving upon it a beautiful orange tree, with every twig and leaf, and each ripe fruit outlined. He looked upon his finished work and was proud, for he knew that even in Italy this ring would be acknowledged a masterpiece of the goldsmith's craft. But the baron came, and took the ring, and was angry because it was so thin and delicate and covered with many scratches! For the baron was a boorish fellow who could not understand the beauty of the work, and desired only that the ring be thick with gold. Then the philosopher was hurt at heart, that his labour should come to such an end.

Again, a nobleman came to the philosopher with a precious oriental stone, upon which an image was engraved. And the nobleman brought a second stone and asked that the philosopher copy the image upon it. The sage set to work, and copied the image so perfectly that no man could tell which was the first, and which the second stone. But the philosopher himself knew that once his hand had slipped less than a hair's breadth, and there was a jot of difference between one jewel and the other. And though the nobleman was greatly pleased with what he had done, the sage had only pain and heartache from his skill, because he knew that he had erred.

And from his skill as a physician, too, he had only pain and heartache. For many sick people came to him, and among them was a man near death. The physician gave him a medicine that he knew was proper for his disease, but the man was so far gone in weakness that he died. And then the people all cried out that it was the physician's potion that had killed him!

And when he came to another sick man and cured him, it was said that the man would have become well in the natural course of things.

So from all of his skill and knowledge, the sage reaped only trouble and anguish. Thus, when he desired a new coat, he called the ablest tailor in the town, and took great pains to teach the man how to make a coat according to the latest fashion; and the tailor at last understood, and made a fashionable jacket, except that he sewed one sleeve somewhat crookedly, and though there was no one in all that region who was enough of a judge of fashion to see that the sleeve was crooked, the philosopher was tortured with shame, for he knew that if he were to appear in that coat in the streets of a Spanish city, the people would at once detect the crooked sleeve, and laugh behind his back.

So the wise man was always troubled and unhappy. The simpleton would come to him laughingly and say, " Why is it that you are always so sad? Here I am a fool, and I have nothing, yet I am cheerful and find joy in life; and you are so wise and so rich, and so unhappy! If God would only let us change places so that I would be the sage, and you the simpleton, then you might be happy, too! "

The philosopher thought that the simpleton was surely mad, and he said, " A wise man might easily fall sick and lose his mind and become a simpleton, but it would be impossible for a fool to become a sage."

The simpleton answered, " Everything is possible to God, he can do anything. In the twinkling of an eye, he might make me wiser than you! " And he laughed, and the philosopher laughed at the words of his mad foolish friend.

The fame of their friendship had spread far and wide. For though there are many fools and many wise men in the world, it is a strange thing for a fool and a wise man to be fast friends through childhood and into manhood. It became known everywhere that in a certain house in a certain town a fool and a philosopher lived together. And even their names were changed, and one was named Fool and the other Philosopher; and so their names were written in the books of the nation: Mr. Fool, and Mr. Philosopher.

One day the king looked through the books, and he came upon those two names together, and he laughed. Then he was curious to see the two men called Fool and Philosopher. But he thought, " If I send suddenly for them to appear at court, the Philosopher may be so frightened that he won't know what to answer, and the Fool may go mad with fear. I'll send a sage to the philosopher, and a simpleton to the fool."

There are plenty of sages in a king's court, but where was he to find a fool to send as messenger to the fool? It happened, however, that the king had appointed a simpleton to be his treasurer, for he knew that if a clever man were made treasurer he might steal the money that was in his charge, while a simpleton would be foolish enough to be honest. So the king gave the treasurer letters to take to Mr. Fool. And he also gave letters to one of his sages, to take to Mr. Philosopher.

The two messengers took the letters and went on their way. They stopped to see the governor of the province where the strange pair lived, and from the governor they received more letters to the fool and philosopher, explaining that the king's message was not a command, but an invitation, and that they might go before the king or stay at home, as they wished, for the king did not wish to frighten them. The messengers told the governor of the great wisdom and riches of the philosopher, and they spoke of the fool who ran about in his ragged cloak, believing it was a fur coat, and a frock coat, and all kinds of coats in one.

The governor said, " If he is so poor, it will not look well for him to come to the king's court." And he took handsome garments and placed them in the carriage of the fool's messenger, for the fool.

When the king's foolish treasurer came to Mr. Fool with the king's letter, the fool said at once, " But you know I can't read! Read it for me! "

" I don't have to read it," the messenger replied. " I can tell you what is in it."

" Then what does it say? "

" It says that the king wants you to come to visit him."

The fool looked at the fool and said, " No fooling? " And the fool answered, " No fooling." At once Mr. Fool bubbled over with joy, and ran to his wife, calling, " My sweet wife, the king has sent for me! "

" What for? " she asked. But he had no time to answer her. He even forgot to ask for his " gold embroidered cloak," but rushed straight into the messenger's carriage, and they started for the court of the king.

As he sat in the carriage the simpleton saw the costly garments that the governor had placed there for him, so he put them on, and as he rode in the king's carriage, clothed in princely garments, his joy streamed up to the very heavens.

In the meantime the king had received news that the governor of that province was dishonest and a traitor, so the king decided to remove him from office at once. He had to choose another governor, and thought, " I must not choose a clever man, for this man was clever, and see what trouble he has brought upon me. It does not take much wisdom to make a good governor, only a good heart, and the will to be just. Any fool can be a governor." And so he decided that since he had a fool for a treasurer, who fulfilled his duties well and gave no trouble at all, he would have another fool for a governor.

And he sent out a decree that the simpleton who was on his way to the palace should be stopped when he came to the gates of the governor's city, and be made governor there.

So it was that when the carriage with the two fools came up to the gates of the governor's city, there were people standing on the walls, and there were banners hanging in the streets, and the path of the carriage was strewn with blossoms. The elders of the city came out to meet the carriage, and they brought a great golden key so heavy that six men bowed beneath its weight. They presented the key of the city to the simple cobbler and said, " Hail to our new governor! "

He looked at them, and smiled, and asked, " But, no fooling? "

" No fooling! " they answered. So with great delight he went to the palace and became governor.

It is said that good fortune makes men wise; then it was revealed that he had enough wisdom to govern, for he ruled with simple honesty, and trusted in the judgement of his heart between what was true and what was false. Soon he became famous throughout the kingdom as the wisest and best of governors. Each day the king heard tales of the marvellous judgement of the cobbler who ruled in the provinces. Then the king sent for him to come and visit the great palace; and when the fool came to the palace, the king received him with honour, and sat down to converse with him. They talked of the ways of government, and the king was greatly pleased with the simple wisdom of the fool. " Tell me," the king asked, " how would you judge between two men who came before you, if each of them declared that he owned the same horse? "

" One of them would be lying," said the fool.

" And how would you find out which one was telling the truth? "

" When I was a cobbler," said the governor, " everyone knew what a great fool I was, and they would come and tell me all sorts of tales, because I believed whatever they told me. But they told so many lies, that it soon became easy for me to know when a man was lying, and when he spoke the truth. All I had to do was to ask them, ' No fooling? ' and they would tell me."

The king was so delighted with the governor that he made him his prime minister, and ordered that a palace be built for him next to the royal palace. It was second in grandeur and beauty only to the palace of the king; and there the cobbler lived.

But when the king's wise messenger came to the philosopher with the king's message, the philosopher was not as quick as the fool to obey. " Remain here overnight," the philosopher said to the messenger, " while we think about what is written in the letter."

That evening he made a feast for his guest, and as they sat over their dinner he thought, " Who am I that the king should send for me? I am only a little man in a little town, and he is a great king over a vast domain, what need has he of me? True, I am wise, but his court is filled with wise men, and he is himself a sage. It cannot be true that the king has sent for me."

Then he said to the messenger, " Tell me, did you receive this letter from the hands of the king himself? "

The messenger said, " No. The letter was given to me by a servant of the king."

Then the philosopher smiled wisely, and asked further, " Tell me, do you often see the king, face to face? "

The messenger answered, " You cannot be familiar with the customs of the palace, or you would know that the king is rarely seen face to face. And when he does appear before the public, he wears ceremonial robes so elaborate that one can hardly see the king."

" Then," said the philosopher, " have you ever seen the king at all? "

The messenger reflected, and answered, " No, now that you ask, I don't think I have ever really seen the king."

The philosopher arose. " It is as I thought," he said. " There is no king."

But the other wise man laughed and asked, " In that case, who rules the kingdom? "

" I knew you would ask me that question," said the philosopher, "and I can answer you, for .I have travelled all over the world and seen many things. There is no king in all the world. In Italy, for example, I saw that the kingdom was ruled by seventy lords who came together and governed as they pleased, and sometimes a new baron would gather an army and overthrow an old lord, then the upstart would be among the seventy governors. And so it is among us. There are powerful men who govern this kingdom, but they hide themselves behind the pretence that we are governed by a king."

The messenger became very thoughtful, and began to believe in the words of the philosopher.

" Tomorrow morning," said the philosopher, " I will prove to you that what I have said is true."

And in the morning the sage said to his guest, " If you will come to the market-place with me, I shall show you how all the world is in error, obeying a king who does not exist."

So they went out, and they came to a soldier who stood on guard at the gate.

" Whom do you serve? " asked the philosopher.

" The king! " the soldier said.

" In all your life, have you ever seen the king? " asked the philosopher.

" Why, no," the soldier said.

Then the philosopher smiled, and whispered to his companion, " See what a fool he is! "

They went further, and met an officer, and they began to talk with him, and then the sage asked him, " Whom do you serve? "

The officer answered, " I serve the king! "

" And have you ever seen him? "

" Why, no," the officer said.

Now the clever messenger was convinced that the philosopher was right. " The whole world is in error! " the messenger cried. " There is no king! Come, let us go out over the world, and show the people how they are mistaken."

So they purchased horses, and set out upon the roads. Wherever they went they asked the people whom they served, and everyone answered, " The king! " The two wise men laughed more and more each day, and told each other that all the world was in error, and that only they two knew the truth: that there really was no king!

And so they travelled until their money was spent; then they sold one of their horses, and then their other horse; they sold their costly garments, and when they had sold everything they owned that was of worth, they became beggars. Still they wandered up and down the roads, begging for scraps of bread and for copper coins, while they whispered to each other, " See how these fools are in error! They believe there is a king! "

It so happened that in their wandering they came to that great city where the cobbler, who was now prime minister, lived in his palace. And in that city there was a holy man, a true wonder-worker who had the power of healing the sick, for he was a Baal Shem, which means a master of the Holy Name.

When the two wise men passed the house of the wonder-worker, they saw many wagons standing in the courtyard, and they saw sick people being carried into the house. Then the philosopher thought that this must be the house of a physician; and since he had himself once been a celebrated physician, he thought, " I will go in and speak with him." So he asked of the people near the house, " Who lives here? "

" It is the house of a Baal Shem," they told him.

Then he broke out into laughter. " Brother," he said to his companion, " these people are even greater fools than we found in the rest of the world, for they believe that a Baal Shem has the power to heal them! But I, who am a physician, know better! "

Their long walk that day had made the two sages hungry, and as they still had a few pence that they had begged, they went to the public kitchen where food can be bought even for a few pence, and they sat down to eat while they talked of the folly of the people who believed in the Baal Shem.

The keeper of the kitchen heard them talking, and became enraged, for the Baal Shem was a very holy man in that city. So the keeper said to them, " Eat what you have bought, and begone, for you cannot talk here against the Baal Shem! "

" You are a fool to believe in this Baal Shem," said the philosopher, " for he is only an imposter who gets gold from the people by mumbling words over their heads! "

At this the cook became terribly angry, and shouted to them to be still. But they would not be still. Just then more people came into the kitchen, and among them was a son of the Baal Shem, and they heard what the philosopher was saying. The cook could contain his anger no more, and he seized a great iron ladle and rushed upon the two wise men; he swung the iron over their heads and shoulders, beating them until their blood ran, and they rushed from the kitchen, howling with pain.

Then the philosopher cried, " We will seek justice against him for this beating! " And they went to complain before a magistrate.

" Why were you beaten? " he asked.

" Because we told them the truth about the Baal Shem! "

" And what is the truth? " asked the magistrate, who was a gentile.

" That the Baal Shem is an impostor and a thief! "

At this, the magistrate ordered them to be thrown into jail.

But the philosopher said to his companion, " We will yet go before a higher court, and receive justice! " So they sat in the jail, and waited. At last their complaints were heard, and they were brought before a higher court. And again they declared that they sought retribution against the cook, who had beaten them because they spoke against a wonder-worker. And again they were thrown into prison. So they complained to a still higher official; and they went from one court to another, until at last they came to the highest court of the land, where they would be heard by the prime minister.

When the prime minister, who was in truth the cobbler, saw the philosopher brought before him he recognized him at once as the friend of his youthful days, though he was no longer dressed in fashionable clothes, but in rags. The sage, however, did not recognize the simpleton, who was now in the majestic robes of a prime minister.

"Don't you know me?" cried the prime minister. "I am the simpleton, the cobbler, your own faithful friend! See, the king has made me prime minister!"

"The king?" said the philosopher. And for the moment he forgot the cause that had brought him to court, and returned to his old folly. "Don't you know that there is no king?" he demanded.

"What are you saying?" cried the minister.

"Have you ever seen the king?"

"I see him every day with my own eyes," said the simple man.

But the philosopher only laughed, and said, "How do you know he is really the king? Do you know him from birth? Did you know his father? Did you know his grandfather, that you are so certain he is the king? Fool, people have told you: this is the king! and you have believed them."

Then the simpleton said, "Remember how we once talked together and you told me that it would be easy for a sage like yourself to lose his wits and become as foolish as I was; but that I, the fool, could never attain wisdom like yours? Now see, I have become very wise, but you have not yet learned to be simple."

Then he ordered splendid garments to be brought for his friend, and they sat down to dinner together, and the prime minister said, "Now tell me, what was the complaint that brought you to the court?"

"I came to seek justice," said the philosopher, "for I was beaten in the public kitchen."

"And why were you beaten?"

"The simpletons believe in a Baal Shem, and I

told them that their wonder-worker was nothing but an impostor, who took their gold."

Just then someone came into the room and said to them, " The devil has sent for you."

At these words, the simpleton began to tremble with fright; he ran from the room, and found his wife, and said, " What shall I do? The devil has sent for me! "

" Don't be frightened," she told him. " We will ask the wonder-worker to help us."

The Baal Shem came at once and spoke a prayer over the prime minister, and purified him. Then the prime minister returned to the room, where the philosopher had remained.

" Why were you so frightened? Why did you run out of the room? " asked the sage.

" Didn't you hear him say the devil had sent for us? "

At this, the philosopher broke into laughter. " My friend," he said, " don't you know that there is no devil? "

The simpleton asked, " Then who was it that sent for us? "

" It must have been my companion," said the wise man. " Perhaps he grew tired of waiting for me so long, and sent a messenger, and told him in jest to say that the devil had sent him."

" If that is so, then would you go with him? " asked the simpleton.

" Why not? " said the philosopher, laughing.

And just then the messenger returned, and said, " The devil has sent for you! " This time the prime minister was not afraid, for he felt the power of the

Baal Shem protecting him. And the philosopher said, " He is surely come from my friend." Then turning to the messenger he asked, " What does he look like, the one who sent you? "

" He has red hair," said the messenger.

" My friend has red hair," said the philosopher, laughing. And he arose.

" Then you are not afraid to go with him? " asked the simpleton.

" Of course not! " cried the sage. " But perhaps it would be well if you told two soldiers to go with me, because after all it may be that some enemies of mine have sent this man, thinking to draw me into harm."

So the prime minister commanded two soldiers to follow them, and the philosopher went out with the strange messenger.

Soon the soldiers returned, and the prime minister asked them what had become of his friend.

The soldiers replied, " We don't know." Then they told him how the strange messenger had led them outside the palace, where the philosopher had met his companion, and in that moment the philosopher, and his companion, and the strange messenger had disappeared.

The prime minister was worried for the fate of his friend, and he sent out searching parties to find the two wise men, but no trace of them could be found.

Then one day as the prime minister was walking in the city he went by the house of the Baal Shem, and he thought, " I will ask the Baal Shem, perhaps he can help me find my friend."

So he went into the house and said to the Baal

Shem, " Do you remember my friend the philosopher who spoke against you? "

" I remember him," said the wonder-worker.

" He has vanished, and I am afraid the devil has taken him," said the simpleton. " Perhaps you can show me where he is? "

The Baal Shem said, " I can show you, but no one else must know."

Then they two went out of the city. And they came to a place that was all loathsome slime filled with crawling beasts and worms. As they approached the filthy pit they heard the screaming and groaning of the two wise men.

They came to the edge of the morass, and they saw the two sages struggling in the oozing mud; their heads would sink below the surface, and again they would lift their mouths out of the filth, and slime would drip from their eyes, and they would cry, " Save us! "

The simple man said to them, " See where the devil has brought you! "

But the philosopher shouted, " It is our enemies who have thrown us into this slime, and they come here and beat us, and set scorpions and snakes in the mud to torture us! There is no devil! Only our enemies among mankind have done this thing! "

" Do you still hold to your foolish philosophy," said the prime minister, " and will you not believe in anything at all? "

" How can we believe in a devil, and a Baal Shem, and a king, when there are no such things on earth! " cried the philosopher, and his mouth was filled with mud.

" Here is the Baal Shem himself," said the prime minister; " and if he can take you out of this pit, will you believe? "

" We will believe," they said.

Then the Baal Shem uttered the Name that is the Secret of Secrets, and no one heard, but in that instant the morass dried, and the mud hardened, and the beasts and snakes were gone, and the two philosophers found themselves standing clean and safe on dry earth.

THE KING'S SON AND THE SERVANT'S SON

WHO HEARD THE MELODY OF ALL THE EARTH'S CREATURES

THERE was a great king whose realm was so wide that a man might walk all the days of his life without coming to the border of the king's lands. This king had a beautiful queen, whose servant was a shrunken old woman with evil eyes. In a cottage near the palace there lived a gardener, with his wife.

It so happened that on the same day, and at the very same hour, a son was born to the queen, and to the gardener's wife. Then the queen's aged servant thought, "What will happen, if I put one child in place of the other? Is there anything within them that causes one child to be kingly, and makes a peasant of the other?" So she took the queen's babe, wrapped him in rough spun sacking, and placed him in the bed of the gardener's wife; then she took the peasant's son, and swaddled him in the silken coverlets of the royal nursery, and placed him in the queen's bed. The children grew, and only the old servant knew that they had been interchanged.

But the boy in the palace felt himself drawn to the soil, and often ran out to play in the garden: there he would help the gardener dig the earth, and plant seeds. He became friends with the child who was thought to be the gardener's son, and took him into the palace to sit with him through his lessons, thus both boys studied together, and the boy from the gardener's cottage was quick to learn languages and the laws of governing a state.

Meanwhile the old servant who had put one child

in place of the other felt her death coming near, and
the secret of the thing she had done troubled her so
that she could not keep it within herself. " There will
be no room for so great a secret in my grave," she
thought. She wanted to tell her secret, but she did
not know to whom to tell it. Then one day as she sat
in her lonely hut she told the secret to the four walls.
The walls told it to the wind, and the wind passed a
man walking in the road, the man heard the secret
and told it to his friend, his friend had a friend, and
each friend had another friend, so that soon the secret,
whispered from one man to another, in the taverns,
over drinking cups, in bed, in the fields and woods,
became known to all the people in the kingdom. Only
the king and queen and the gardener and his wife
knew nothing of the secret.

For if the king had known, what might he have
done? He could not trust in the truth of a thing that
was whispered, therefore he could not return each
child to his place, for he might never be sure which
of them was truly his son.

But one day a soldier in the palace became drunk,
and talked with the prince and said to him, " You are
not really the prince, but the son of the gardener. It
is whispered all over the kingdom that the other boy
is the true prince. And I tell you this as a warning, so
that if ever there may be an uprising to place him
upon the throne, you are warned."

The false prince was troubled, but would not believe the tale. Nevertheless, he thought it would be
better if the gardener's boy were out of the kingdom.
He began to bring troubles upon the gardener, that
he might flee the land. In secret, the prince would

creep into the garden and destroy the plants, so that the poor man would have to work night and day to earn his bread; and even then, his crops were spoiled, and the king was dissatisfied with him, and his life was miserable.

Not long after that, the king died, and the false prince became the ruler of the country. Then he was even more harsh with the gardener, who was fallen into poverty and illness from overwork. The gardener complained to a friend, saying, " I don't know why my work goes against me. And the king has taken a dislike to me, so that nothing I do pleases him."

The friend took pity on the gardener, and told him what everyone knew. " If you will send your boy out of the country," he said, " the king will look kindly upon you."

The gardener did not want to send the boy away, but if things went on as they were, they would all starve. So he told the boy, " It is whispered among the people that you are truly the old king's son, that the present king is my son, and that in childhood you were put one in place of the other. Now it is too late to remedy the wrong, and the king fears you will seize the throne that may be yours by right. Therefore you must go out of the country." He gave the boy all the money he could borrow, and the boy went into exile.

His heart was bitter, for he thought, " I have been driven from the country where I should truly be ruler." But again he thought, " Perhaps the whole story is an old wives' tale, and a falsehood; how might I ever know that I was truly born a king? "

He was sore and lonely, banished from his country.

" For if I am indeed the king's son," he thought, " I should certainly not have been banished. And if I am not the king's son, then why must I suffer this punishment? "

In his bitterness and loneliness away from home he sought for amusement; he went into the wineshops and drank; he went among women, and was gay.

Meanwhile the false king governed with a mighty hand, and wherever a rumour of his true birth arose, he punished those who were heard to repeat it, so that not even a whisper of truth was allowed in the land. Nevertheless, he had dreams. He dreamed that he must give up his kingdom, and go away, wherever he might be led. Twice he had the same dream.

On the third day he summoned his courtiers to go on a hunt with him; they rode into the woods, and came to a beautiful place where the sun shone among the trees, and upon a pool of water. " Let us rest here awhile," said the king. He dismounted from his horse, and lay down to sleep beneath a tree.

He did not know whether he was awake or asleep, but felt his mind troubled, and it was as if the boy who had been his playmate in the garden and in the schoolroom stood by his side and talked with him. " It was an unjust thing to banish me," the boy said. And the king thought to himself, " Surely it was unjust, for if he is the king's true son, the kingdom is his by right, and if he is the gardener's son, why should he be punished? " The false king was deeply troubled in his thoughts, he dreamed again; then he opened his eyes, and saw the sky through the leaves of the trees.

" I will not hunt today," he said. And he called the

courtiers, and cried to them, " Turn home! I will not hunt! "

The courtiers saw that the king was troubled, and in a dark mood, so they mounted on their horses, and turned their heads homeward. The king arose after them, but when he went to mount his steed, he could not find him. Then he saw the horse not far away, nibbling among the trees, and the king went after the horse.

The exiled prince had spent all of his money in drink and in easy living. Now when he was poor and could no longer drink away his sorrow, the thought came to him, " And if I were truly a prince, would I live as I have been living? " That night he slept in a field, and dreamed. He dreamed that he came to a fair in a neighbouring city, and that a man approached him and asked him if he wanted to work. And he knew that no matter how lowly the toil, he must do it.

When he awoke the true prince remembered this dream, though often dreams go out of the mind. Yet he thought, " How should I, who am born a prince, become a low servant to the first man who asks my hire? " And instead he begged money, and bought drink.

But at night he dreamed again, and saw the fair, and heard a voice saying, " Whatever work is offered you, you must do " And though he would not go that day either, the dream came to him a third time.

Then he sold the fine garments which he still wore, and put on the clothes of a wayfarer, and went to the market. He came to the city at night, and slept there. He arose very early in the morning and went out into the road. Soon a merchant came riding towards him, crying, " You, there, do you want to work? "

The prince knew that he must answer " Yes," and do whatever the man asked of him. So he answered, " Yes. What kind of work have you? "

" I need a herdsman," the man said. " Come with me."

The prince was sorry that he must go, for he was delicately made, and he was frightened of the rough manners and the angry voice of his master. He asked, " Must I drive the herds myself? "

" I have other drivers waiting," the merchant told him. And they went to a courtyard where a number of servants waited. Then the merchant gave the prince a herd of cattle to watch, and all the herdsmen with their flocks started on the highway that led out of the city, while the prince drove his cattle along with the others. The merchant rode on his horse, carrying a heavy stick in his hand; he rode up and down from one herd to another, shouting at the men and at the beasts with great cruelty, and sometimes knocking at them with his stick.

Often he rode up to the prince, urging him roughly onward, and the prince shrank with fear, for his skin was delicate, and he thought that if the merchant struck him with the heavy stick he would surely bleed.

After some hours they stopped by the wayside, and the merchant took bread out of a sack and gave it to the herdsmen; they divided the bread amongst themselves, and ate. The prince ate with them; when they had eaten, they started again on their journey.

They came to a forest. As they were passing through the forest, two of the prince's cattle turned away from the herd, and ran among the trees. The prince ran to catch them, but as soon as he came near them the beasts ran farther into the woods, and in a few moments they led him to where the trees grew so thick that he could no longer see his companions, nor could they see him. Then the prince thought, " If I return without the cattle, the master will kill me; and if I remain here in the wood, I'll be killed by wild beasts." But he was so afraid of the master that he thought he would rather be killed by wild beasts, and he ran farther into the forest after the two cows.

Night came, but he had not caught them. He heard the cries of the forest creatures, and when he thought that he must pass the night alone in that wild place, he felt himself frozen with fear. At last he climbed up into a tree, and lay among the branches, and slept.

At dawn he was awakened by the howling of wild beasts. Then he heard a sound like soft laughter. He looked down from the branches, and he saw the two cows standing quietly underneath his tree. The prince climbed down, but as soon as he came near the cows they began to run again, and he went after them. The cattle found grass, and stopped to nibble the grass, and he crept close, but the instant he was near enough to seize them, they ran again. So he followed after them all day, farther into the heart of the forest, until there were no paths anywhere, but only the tangled ways of a great wilderness inhabited by beasts that had no fear of men.

The prince was more frightened than before; but when night came he saw a great tree standing alone near a pool of water; he climbed into that tree to sleep.

As he reached the wide branches he was startled,

for he saw another man sitting in the tree. And though the prince was startled, he was glad, for now he would not be so lonesome in the forest.

The prince spoke to the man. " Who are you? "

" A man," he answered. And asked, " Who are you? "

The prince answered, " A man."

The man said, " Where do you come from? "

" Two cows escaped from my herd," the prince answered, " and I followed them into the forest but could not catch them." Then he said, " Where do you come from? "

" My horse ran away," the man said, " and I followed him but could not catch him."

Then they swore to remain together in the forest, and to be friends even when they came out of the forest. And they went to sleep.

Towards dawn, they were awakened by a great laughter. It was not like human laughter, but it was like the sound the prince had heard softly the night before; this time it was so loud that it seemed as though all the leaves in the forest, and all the branches, shook with laughter, while all the wild beasts howled with strange glee. The very branches in which they slept rocked upon the sounds, and the prince, awakening, cried out:

" What is that laughter? "

" Don't be afraid," said his companion. " This is not the first night I have passed in this place. With every coming of dawn, this laughter comes."

Still, the prince was uneasy, for where men lived there had never been such laughter. It seemed to him that this must be a place inhabited by devils, for where else might there be a whole world of laughter? He looked down from the tree, thinking he would see devils below him, but instead he saw his two cows standing there peacefully, and near them stood a horse.

Then the prince and his companion went down from the tree, but at once the animals began to run away from them; the horse ran one way, and the cows another, and each man went after his own, so they were separated from each other.

When the prince had gone a long while after the cows, he saw something on the ground before him; he picked it up: it was a sack filled with bread. He was very pleased to find such a thing in a forest where no men came; he took the sack on his back.

After a time he came quite close to the cattle, but before he could seize them, a little man ran across his way. He was frightened, but again he was glad to see a human being. The old man asked, "How did you get here?" And the prince replied, "How did you get here?"

Then the old man said, "It is simple enough for me to answer, for I was born here, and so was my father before me, and so was his father. But how did you get here?"

When the prince heard this, he knew that the creature could not be a human being, as no men came so far into the forest. But he answered. "My cows ran away, and I followed them."

The gnome laughed softly at him, but it was laughter that he thought he had heard before. "These are not cows," the little man said; "they are only your sins. You have pursued them long enough, and your

punishment is over; now it is time for you to receive
that which is yours. Come with me."

The prince walked after the wood-sprite, but
he was afraid to speak with him, thinking, "Perhaps he is a demon. He may open his mouth and
swallow me!"

After they had gone a short distance, the prince
saw his companion of the night before, whom he had
lost. He motioned to the man not to go near the
wood-sprite, and then lagged behind and said to the
man, "That is not a human being at all, but a creature of the woods. Who knows what he may be!"
Meanwhile the man saw that the prince carried a sack
of bread on his shoulders, so he cried out, "Give me
bread to eat! It is many days since I have eaten!"

When he heard this, the prince thought, "We are
in a wilderness where there is no food." So he said
to the man, "What will you give me for bread?" The
man thought, "What is worth more than bread in
the wilderness?" and no riches seemed great enough to
buy the bread. "I'll sell you myself!" he cried. "I'll
be your eternal slave, only give me bread!"

Then the prince gave the man bread to eat, and
promised to share the food with him as long as it
remained, and took the man for his slave; even if they
would come out of the wilderness, the man promised,
he would remain his slave.

So they went on; the gnome went first, and the
prince followed him, and the slave followed after the
prince.

They came to a place where there were no more
trees, but before them lay a morass of oozing mud filled
with writhing snakes and hissing scorpions.

The prince cried, " How will we pass over this place? "

The little creature smiled on him and said, " If you cannot even pass over this place, how will you get into my house? " And he showed them his house, that hung high in the air.

The prince and his slave stared in wonder. But the being took each of them by the hand, and went through the air with them into his house.

He gave them pillows to lie upon, and showed them a table that was laden with wonderful foods and fine drink. " Eat and drink," he said, and he went from the room.

Then the slave had to serve his master with food, and he was sorry and angry for having sold himself for bread only an hour before, when now he had plenty. He grumbled and he sighed, saying, " Oh, that a person such as I should become a lowly slave."

The prince said to him, " What were you before, that slavehood is so far beneath you? "

The man said, " I was a king. But perhaps slavery is my true and deserved place."

" Why do you say that? " asked the prince.

Then the man, who was really the gardener's son who had in childhood been changed for a prince, told the true prince how there had been rumours in his kingdom that his throne belonged to another, and how he had sent that other into exile.

" Then I had dreams," the man said. " In my dreams it seemed to me that the exiled one was truly king, and that I should give up my kingdom, and go out, and go wherever I was led. At first I did not heed the dreams, but one day I went into the forest to hunt, and I dreamed again, and when I awoke I followed my horse into the woods. And so I became your slave."

The prince listened, and knew who it was that spoke, but himself remained silent.

At night the little old man came to them and showed them their beds, and they went to sleep. But toward dawn they were once more awakened by the strange laughter; this time it was louder than ever before; the branches of the trees were broken by the gales of laughter, and the house rocked as upon the waves of laughter. The slave said to the true prince, " Perhaps if you will ask the little man, he will tell you what sort of laughter that is."

When the wood-sprite came to them, the prince said, " What is the cause of the laughter that comes at dawn? "

" Oh," said the little man, " that is only Day laughing at Night, for at that hour Night asks of the Day: ' Why is it that when you come, I no longer have a name? ' And then the Day laughs, and it is Day. That is the laughter that is heard at dawn."

Still the prince wondered.

During the day they had great pleasure, eating, and drinking; the prince leaned on the pillows, and the slave served him. Then they slept. But that night they were awakened by the voices of beasts. They heard the booming of the lion, the panther's shriek, the twittering and crying of birds, and the calls of all the wild creatures of the forest; the sounds of the beasts and the birds became louder and wilder; never before had there been such a furious noise of howling and barking and roaring and shrieking together. The men listened. But after they had listened well awhile, they were no longer terrified by the sounds. " Do you hear? " the prince said, " it is sometimes like a song." They listened, and at moments the howling and shrieking and roaring came to them as a strange and beautiful song. They listened more eagerly, and then the song became clearer, and each moment it became more beautiful, until to hear it was a pleasure greater than all the pleasures that men know on earth. The melody was so wildly beautiful that they wanted to remain there forever, listening.

Then the servant begged the prince to ask the wood-being what sort of music it was that they heard. And when the little man came into the room, the prince asked him, " Where does that singing come from? "

" The sun has woven a new silver gown for the moon," the wood-being said, " and therefore all the creatures of the wood are singing. For you know that the moon is their friend, since the moon lights their way at night when they must go forth in search of food. And so they have made a new melody for the moon."

" I have never heard anything so wonderful as their song," the prince said.

" Haven't you? " cried the gnome. " Then listen! I have a flute that was given to me by my father, who had it from his father, who had it from his father before him. It is made of strange reeds and wondrous leaves, and you have only to touch any bird or beast with the wand, and the creature will begin to sing a music that is more beautiful than this."

Just then the laughter that came before dawn was heard again; the whole world laughed, and day came.

The little man went out of the room. Then the prince cried, " I would like to have that magic reed he spoke of! " and he arose and searched every corner of the chamber, but could not find the wand.

When the prince had finished seeking, the gnome returned and said to them, " It is time that you returned to the world of men."

" How can we go there? " said the prince.

" I'll show you the way," the gnome answered. Then the little man took the magic flute with him, and he led them out of the house that hung in the air, over the morass of snakes and scorpions, back to dry earth.

" Which way shall we go? " asked the prince.

" Go to the land of the Foolish People With The Wise King. For there you will come into your right," he said to the prince. " And with your servant, you will know how to deal." Then he took the reed from his pocket and gave it to the prince, saying, " This is for you."

The prince took the flute with delight, and looked about for an animal whom he might touch with the wand, that they might again hear the song of the wild creatures. But he could not find a single beast.

" Now you must go," the wood-sprite said.

" Which way shall we go? " asked the prince.

The little man raised his arm and pointed, and they went that way.

They went a long time through the wilderness, always seeking some animal who might be made to sing, but they saw no living creature.

At last the prince and his servant came to the land of the Foolish People With The Wise King. The kingdom was girt around by a high wall, and there was only one gate in the wall, through which strangers might pass into the kingdom. They followed the wall for a long time until they came to the gate.

But the guards at the gate would not allow them to enter, for the king of that country had died, and though his son who ruled after him was learned when compared to other men, he was so little wise when compared to his father that the country was now called the land of the Wise People With The Foolish King. And the former king had commanded that only the man who could again make the country known as the land of the Foolish People With The Wise King should be crowned to succeed him. So no one was allowed to enter the country unless he undertook to make it the land of the Wise King.

" Can you do that? " the guards asked of the prince.

" How can I do that? " thought the prince, and he was afraid to try. His slave said, " Let us go home." But as they stood there another stranger, riding a horse, came and stopped by the gate to the kingdom. Then as the prince saw the horse he thought, " Now I can try the magic flute! " and he ran up and touched the horse with the reed. At once the animal began to sing the wildly sweet song of the beasts, and all who heard were astonished.

The stranger who rode the horse cried, " Sell me that magic reed! " But the prince would not part with it.

" Fool! " said the stranger, and he was as one who was known to them, " Of what use can the reed be to you? You will go about making jokes with it, and perhaps someone will give you a gulden for your folly! Rather become a man than a child. I have a thing I can give you in exchange for the wand."

" What is it? " asked the prince.

" I can give you the secret of understanding the meaning of the thing within the thing. It is a secret that was given me by my father, who had it from his father, who had it from his own father before him. And I have never told it to anyone."

The prince was satisfied, and gave the man the flute, and the man went aside with him and taught him to know the meaning that is at the heart of each thing.

And when the prince understood how one thing comes from another, he returned to the gate, and knew that he must go in and try to give back to the land its former name. So he was taken before the court of noblemen who were the judges of wisdom, and they said to him, " Know, that we ourselves are no fools, but the king who died was so marvellously wise that against him we were as fools, and the country was called the land of the Foolish People With The Wise King. When the king died he left a son who was no simpleton, but against our wisdom he seemed as simple as a fool, so the land was changed and called the land of the Wise People With The Foolish King. Now whoever brings back the former name may be crowned our ruler, but if you would test your wisdom for this task you must go into the garden that was left by our wise king."

He was told that the king's garden was a wondrous place where things of gold and silver grew, but that since the king's death no man had been able to re-main in the garden, for as soon as he entered, he was pursued, and he would run, and run faster, but he would be pursued until he ran out of the garden, and pursued until he was far away.

" Who is it that runs after him? " asked the prince.

" No one knows. No man has ever seen his pursuers in the garden. But those who have tried to remain there have come running from the place, scarcely alive."

" Are they beaten by the pursuers? " the prince asked.

" They are not badly beaten, but they are frightened, and ill with running."

The prince was taken to the garden; he saw that there was a wall around it, with a wide-open gate in the wall, for such a garden needed no guards.

And as he was about to enter the garden, the prince noticed a statue that stood outside the gate. He went up to the statue and saw that it was the image of a king, and on the stone it was written that the king had lived long ago, and there had been war until his reign, and war after his reign, but while he ruled there had been peace.

Then the prince, who understood the meaning within each thing, knew that this statue would protect him, and that if he were pursued he had only to come near the statue, and he would be safe. He knew also that if he caused the statue to be brought into the garden, there would be no more pursuit in the garden.

He went through the gate, and saw a strangely beautiful place, where all the trees and flowers and grass that grew were of gold and silver and other precious metals. But at once he felt himself being pursued. So he went and stood near the statue, and the noise of his pursuers was gone, and he had not been touched, but was calm and safe. Then the prince called his slave and told him to take the statue into the garden.

And now he walked about in the midst of the garden, and all was peaceful and calm. When the noble judges came he led them into the garden, and they saw that he had brought peace into that place.

"Truly," they said, "you have proven your wisdom. But for this proof alone we cannot make you our king. There is another thing that you must do." And they took him into a great room in the palace. High at the end of the room stood a throne that was richly carved of precious wood, upon the throne were carven all the beasts and the birds that lived within the kingdom. Before the throne there was a couch, and near the couch stood a table, and on the table was a seven-branched candelabrum. Seven ways went out from the throne, and upon each way there stood a marvellous beast or bird: on one path there stood a lion of gold, on another an iron panther, a silver eagle was upon the third, and so on each way there stood a different creature.

"In former times," the nobleman said, "the king sat upon his throne, and the candles burned, and he looked down these seven ways and saw all the ends of his kingdom, and knew all that was happening and all that might take place; and each night when the moc arose the beasts and the birds that guard the seve ways would raise their voices and sing a wildly sweet melody. But now the king is dead, the candles do not burn, the paths are dim, and the beasts have become ferocious so that no man may come near them, but they open their mouths and swallow him."

Then the prince, who understood the meaning

within each thing, went up to the carven throne and looked well upon it and saw that it was made of the same wood as his magic flute, and he saw that the throne was perfect except for a small piece that was missing from a carven creature at the top of the chair. Then he knew that the former king had taken that piece from its place and hidden it, wisely knowing that when a wise man would come he would find each thing, and put each thing again in its proper place. So the prince looked about the room, and looked behind the throne, and found the missing piece and put it back in its place; then he sat upon the throne.

The prince looked at the table before him, and saw that it was moved a hair's breadth from the central point where all the seven ways came together, and he ordered his slave to place the table back where it belonged; and then he saw that the seven-branched menorah had been moved, and when that was placed in the centre of the table the candles burned again.

And by their light, the prince saw that each of the creatures that stood in the seven ways had been moved a hair's breadth from his place, and he ordered them to be put back in their proper places. Then, when all things were restored to order, it was midnight, and the beasts and the birds all opened their mouths and began to sing the wild sweet melody that all creatures sing to the moon.

The prince was crowned king, and then he said to his servant, " Now I understand that I was truly born the son of a king, and you were born the son of a servant."

THE WIND THAT OVERTURNED THE WORLD

AND THE KINGDOM OF MONEY-WORSHIPPERS

IN a place beyond the habitations of men there lived a master of prayer. His house was hidden in the forest; there was a body of water in his domain, and by the water grew fruit-laden trees; there he passed his days singing in joyous worship of Heaven.

Sometimes he would leave his retreat to go into the world of men. He would approach one person or another, and begin to talk with him. Mostly he would speak to humble workmen and tradesmen, but rich men, too, had heard him.

" What do you live for? " he would ask.

Some would answer, " To eat and to drink "; others would answer, " To die "; but the Master would prove to them that man lived only for joy, and that man owed his joy to Heaven.

" Come with me," he would say, " and I will show you how to live."

One by one he brought people to his place in the forest; they bathed in the water, they ate of the fruit, they sang, and their worship was purest joy. The master knew the needs of each of his followers; those who had been poor were sometimes given garments of gold, and the rich were happy in beggar's rags.

But in the world of men it came to be known that there was a Master who caused men to leave their wives and their brothers while they followed him, so a great cry was set up that the Master must be captured.

This they could not do, for he cleverly disguised

himself, once as a merchant, another time as a soldier, and a third time as a wanderer; no man could tell who he was, until the Master had won the man to his will.

And already among the Master's followers there were some who lived so perfectly in his ways that they too went among men, and brought away people to live as they lived.

In that time there was a strange kingdom inhabited by a people who believed only in riches. Among them, a man was judged according to the sum of money that he possessed. Each year, each citizen would tell the measure of his possessions, and accordingly receive his rank. Those who had no money, or very little, might not even call themselves men, but were ranked as beasts and birds: some were dogs, some cattle, some mules, and they had to serve those who had gold. The richer might call themselves men, and if they had a great sum of money they were noblemen, and if they had a still greater sum they were kings.

There, no one had any thought but to get riches, thus a dog wanted to become a horse, and a horse a lion, and a lion a man, and a man a nobleman, and a nobleman a king. They knew no right or wrong, except the right of riches, so that the country was filled with thieves and bandits who sought to become kings by stealing money. The noblemen and kings employed great armies of men-beasts as soldiers to protect their treasuries, but nevertheless the land was filled with theft and violence.

When the Master's followers heard of that country they said, " Let us go there and see if we can win the people from their folly." So a band of them came to the land where money was worshipped.

They could not find anyone who would stop and listen to them, but at last they spoke to a poor little creature huddled naked in the street. He was not even a man, but was of the rank of a sparrow.

As they began to speak of the folly of riches, he cried, " I have no time to listen to you! "

" What have you to do? " they asked.

" I must prepare to go on a journey, for we have heard of a land where gold may be made out of the earth! " he said. " There I too may become a king, or even a god, according to our laws. Who knows, I may yet win the rank of a star, and I may become that supreme being, the moon. For it is the moon, you know, that makes gold on earth, and if I get enough gold out of the earth I may become the moon, and then I can make all the earth into gold! "

" Where is that land? " they asked of him.

" It is among high mountains, far from the other peoples of the world. We will build our cities on the peaks of those mountains, and make strong walls so that none may enter and steal our gold, and there will be but one secret path upon each mountain leading to each of our cities. And there I, too, may become a god! "

With these words he ran from them, and they saw that all the people were leaving the city.

The disciples returned to their Master and told him of the kingdom of folly where rich men called themselves stars and moons and even gods. The Master cried, " I had feared that they would call themselves gods! " And he determined to go to the new domain of the money-worshippers and try to rid them of their folly.

He came to the guards who stood at the foot of the mountains, and began to speak of the folly of worshipping riches. But the guards, who were only of the rank of hounds and wolves, were filled with the desire to get gold and become men; they could not listen to the Master, but could only stare at the portraits of their kings and gods which they always carried about with them, for the love of riches was grown so deep that they could not imagine a world where things might be otherwise.

Then, seeing that it was of no use to speak with the guards, the Master went by them; he passed through the secret path up the mountain, and came into the city.

In that city were many merchants who often journeyed through the world to trade with other peoples, and on such voyages they had heard of a Master who stole men from their accustomed lives but could not himself be caught. And now as the Master went up to one man and another in that city, and spoke, he found none who would hear him, for their folly was so deeply grown; nevertheless it was soon whispered that the Master of dangerous words was come into the city.

" How did he come here? " they cried, but none could tell. And he was so cleverly disguised that he could not be caught.

Meanwhile these same merchants brought news of a great warrior who went from one nation to another, conquering. It was his custom when he came within fifty miles of a city to send his warriors with a message demanding surrender. If the people submitted to his will he did their city no harm, but marched further; but if the city would not surrender, he made war, and slaughtered its people.

" This same conqueror is coming toward our mountains! " the merchants cried; and all the money-worshippers were terrified that he would take away their riches. But the merchants said, " It is not gold that he seeks, only power over the world." Then they were afraid for their lives, for they could not surrender their city to an infidel who did not believe in riches, and if they did not surrender their city, he would kill them all!

They prayed to their rich men-gods, and they took little beast-men and bird-men and burned them upon altars before these gods; but the sacrifices were of no avail; the warrior came nearer to their kingdom.

" Where shall we turn for help? " they cried. Then one merchant, who had travelled far, said, " There is a land where every man is a god. Surely they can help us." And he told of a country whose people were so rich that the poorest among them was rich enough according to the measures of the money-worshippers to be a god. " Even their steeds," he said, " are of the degree of angels, for their mounts are studded with jewels so rich as to make them of angel's rank. Let us send emissaries to those gods and beg them to help us."

The Master heard of their plan, and he thought, " I will go once more to the mountain cities and try to draw the people away from their folly." Then he came again and began to speak with a guard, but the guard could talk of nothing but the terrible Conqueror.

" Have you no power against him? " the Master said.

" We have sent emissaries to the land where men

are gods, and those gods will help us," the guard said.

Then the Master laughed. " But they are only men like yourselves! " he exclaimed, " and they cannot help you at all. Leave off your foolish talk of gods, for there is only one God, and rich and poor are alike to him, and only he can help you against the Conqueror."

At first the guard would not listen to him, but as he continued to speak, the guard said, " And what if I listen to you, I am only one." Then the Master was pleased, and he went to another guard, and talked to him until that guard said, " And what if I listen to you, I am only one." So he went until he had spoken to all the guards and they had answered him. Then he went into the city, and after he had talked for a long while to a man in the city, the man also said, " And what if I listen to you, I am only one." Thus, because the people were terribly afraid of the Conqueror, the Master was able to make them listen to him. But each time they spoke of the Conqueror, he said, " What Conqueror? Can it be that same Hero whom I knew at the court of the king? "

At last it came to the ears of the gods who ruled the city that the famous Master was among them, talking to the people. They ordered that he be captured and brought before them. And though he disguised himself in many different ways, he was caught and brought before the gods, and to them also he said, " What folly it is to send to the kingdom of gods for help. They are only men like yourselves, and can do no more than yourselves, for no man can stand before the Conqueror."

" What do you know of him? " they asked.

" I know," he said. " For there was a Hero in the
court of a King whom I served. That King possessed
a marvellous image made in the form of a Hand, perfectly made with all five fingers and with the marking
of the faint and the deep lines that are found on the
human hand, and by these markings one might see
the form of every land in the world, as it had been
from the beginning of creation, and as it will be at the
end of time; and on that Hand one might see all that
would happen to each country and each city, and to
every man, for the lines and the markings upon the
Hand were signs by which one might read; and the
rivers and waters of all places were shown there, and
the highways that went from one place to another,
and even the hidden ways were shown there, so that
from that Hand I was able to know the secret path
into your own city, and by that Hand I know the
secret paths into all your other cities, and I know the
ways from this world into other worlds, and I know
the ways that lead up into the heavens, for there is
one way by which Elijah went from the earth to
heaven, and there is another way that Moses went, and
Henoch went by still another path: and they were all
marked upon that Hand.

" There, too, one might see the fate of cities as
they were, and are, and shall be; I have seen Sodom
as it was before it fell, and as it is now; and I have
seen your city, and so I have seen your emissaries go
out to the city where all men are gods, and I have seen
that your emissaries and the men of that city too will
come to a woeful end."

When the elders heard him speak in this way they

thought, " Surely no man can have imagined such a thing, and it must all be true." They looked on their own hands, and saw that they were covered with lines and mysterious markings.

" Bring us to the King who possesses the wondrous Hand! " they cried. " Perhaps he will show us where to find gold! "

Then the Master smiled. " Still you can think of nothing but gold! " he said. " Think rather of how to save yourselves, for gold is of no worth to that King."

But they cried, " Nevertheless, bring us to him, and we will believe as you believe."

Then the Master said, " I do not know myself where the King is to be found, and I will tell you why that is so. Once I lived in the court of this King; he had a queen, and an only daughter, and the King sought a husband for his daughter.

" Now in the King's court there were six ministers: the Sage, who was the master of all wisdom and the keeper of the marvellous Hand; the Counsellor, who was the master of words and melodies; the Companion, who was the dear friend of the King, and each carried with him the portrait of the other and looked upon it when they were separate, for in each portrait was such a power that to look upon it was to grow love for him that was pictured there; the fourth minister was the Treasurer in whose keep were the staff of jewels and the cap of precious stones and all the treasures of the King; the fifth minister was the Warrior, and to him the King had given the marvellous Sword, for this Sword had three powers: if it were but raised against the enemy, all the leaders of the enemy fled, but if the army of the enemy tried to do battle without its leaders, one had but to lean the sword sidewards, and the enemy all fell dead, and if it was leaned to the other side the enemies withered, and their skins dried and fell from them; and I, the Master of Prayer, was the King's sixth minister.

"To each of us the King had shown the secret place where we might replenish our innermost power, for the source of each sort of strength was marked upon that wondrous Hand; then each day we would retire, each minister to his place, to replenish his innermost power. The Sage went one way to the source of wisdom, and the Counsellor went another way to the source of the word, the Treasurer went to the source of riches, the Hero to the source of strength, and I went my way to the source of prayer.

"One day the King asked of me, 'Whom shall I choose as husband for my daughter?' Then I said, 'Let her marry the Warrior!'

"The King was pleased at my answer, and the Daughter and the Hero were married. Then a boy child was born to them who was marvellously beautiful and so wise that before he could speak he understood all things, and this anyone might see, for when a jest was spoken, he laughed.

"But one day when we had all gone away from the palace, each minister to the source of his power, there came a whirlwind that overturned the world, making desert where ocean had been, and turning the dry land into sea. The wind came into the King's palace, but did not move a feather from its place. It went directly to the room where the Princess sat with her Babe, snatched the child from the arms of its mother, and fled. The Princess ran after the wind, seeking her child. And so she ran, and no one knew whither. Then the Queen ran after the Princess, and lost sight of her, and ran another way, and no one knew whither. And after the Queen, the King ran, and no one knew whither.

" When we returned, each man from his own place, we found no one in the palace; then each man set out another way in search of the King and his kin. The wondrous Hand was gone, for the whirlwind had overturned all things, and not one of us could find his way again to the place of the source of his power, yet each of the ministers still had in him a power that was more than that of any other man in the world. Therefore if this Conqueror is that same Hero of our kingdom, no one can stand against him."

When the gods of the money-worshippers heard these words they would not let the Master leave them, for they feared the Conqueror.

Soon the Warrior was fifty miles from the city; then he sent his messengers to demand that the city surrender. The money-worshippers ran to the Master and said, " If this is indeed your friend the Hero, can you not help us? "

The Master asked them, " Will not your riches help you? "

" He refuses riches," they said.

Then the Master decided to go and see whether the Conqueror was indeed his friend the Hero. He went out to the invading army and spoke to one of the warriors. " Who is your leader? " he asked, " and how did he come among you? "

" That is a strange story," the warrior replied. " For

once there was a whirlwind that upset an entire kingdom, and made desert into ocean and the sea into
dry land. After the wind had passed, all the people
came together, but their King was gone. So they asked,
' How shall we choose a king? ' And they asked again,
' What quality is in a king, more than in any other
man? '

" Some said, ' Honour! For even the dead, who
have no use for food, or gold, or beautiful garments,
still demand that honour be paid to their memory.'
Then they who sought honour in a king formed a
band and went off together. On their way they met a
caravan of gypsies; an aged man was being carried
at the head of the caravan. He was blind, and crooked,
and his voice was harsh, and he was angry with his
bearers; though he cursed them aloud, his followers
honoured him, for of all his brothers and sisters and
their many descendants he was the eldest, and therefore the head of their tribe. When the people saw
what great homage was paid to the gypsy, they said to
him, ' Be our king! ' So he growled and cursed them
also, and they went after him, and found a land suitable to them, and settled there to serve their king.

" But another part of the people declared that not
honour, but death was the greatest of all things, for all
men, and beasts, and even the trees and the fruit upon
the trees ended in death; so they sought a murderer
to be their king. They heard a terrified screaming and
asked, ' What has happened? ' ' A man has killed his
father and his mother! ' they were told. ' Such a man
must be the greatest of murderers! ' they cried, and
they made him their king. They sought a land between two mountains, where thieves and bandits

dwelt; there they lived, while the murderer ruled over them.

" Some said, a king should be more delicate than all other people, and so they went to seek for a king who did not eat the foods that other people ate. Yet others said, ' Men should multiply on earth, and because of beauty, children are born.' So they sought for a beautiful woman to rule over them. Still others said, ' It is by his power of speech that man is different from the beasts '; and they sought for a marvellous speaker, and in a market-place they found a madman who talked to himself in seven languages, and never stopped talking. Him they made king.

" There were still others among us who said that joy is the greatest thing in the world, and they found a drunkard in a dirty shirt, he lay in the road and lifted a bottle of wine to his mouth, and he sang; so they made him their king, and they went to a land where grape-vines grew, and settled in that land.

" Some sought for a wise man to rule over them; and at last there were those who said that strength is the greatest of all things among men. I was of that group. We went until we found a giant who could eat an ox and drink a barrel of ale at a single meal, and him we made our king. Wherever we passed, people fled before us. But one day there came a Hero who did not run from us, instead he went among us and drew his sword, then our warriors fled from him, and our carts were tumbled from the highway, and our king turned and ran. So we went up to the Hero and said to him, ' Be our king! ' He became our king, and set out to conquer the world. It is not to rule the world that he seeks, but something otherwise. And

when a city will not surrender to him, he lifts his
sword. And this sword has three powers —"

Then the Master knew that the Hero was indeed
his old friend, and he sent his name to the Hero. The
Hero called for him, he went to the Hero's tent, where
with great joy they recognized each other, and cried,
" At last we are come together again! "

But after a moment the Warrior asked the Master,
" Have you found any of our old companions? "

The Master said, " I have sought everywhere, and
I came upon the places where all of them had passed,
but I found none of them. One day I went by a hill,
and the hill was covered with green grass, and at the
top of the hill there was a golden shrine as if the sinking sun had come to rest and remained there; I went
up the hill, and found the King's crown lying there,
and the winds moved slowly about the hilltop and
murmured a majestic melody; but the King was not
there, he had passed, and I could not find him. On
another day I walked across a dreary waste land where
there was no tree, or bush, or blade of grass, and
all the earth was parched; then I saw a tiny drop of
blood upon the ground, and then another, and each
drop was like a tear; then I came to a pool of blood,
and faintly, as if from the bottom of the pool, I heard
the chanting of a dirge; then I knew that the Queen
had passed that way and wept tears of blood for
the loss of her loved ones, but I could not find her
there.

" I went further, and I came to a fair meadow, and
in the meadow was a tiny stream that was as white as
lamb's wool; and when I came near I saw that it was
a stream of milk, and it made a murmuring sound as

it flowed, a sound like the humming of a lullaby. Then I knew that the Princess had passed that way, and I sought for her but could not find her.

" At last I came to a desert, and in the sands were the footprints of a child's naked feet, and as I went I saw something that glittered like a sun-ray in the sand; I stooped, and found a golden hair of the child. And all about me, in the still air, there hovered a breath of sound, as of a child singing in the womb. Then I sought for the child, but could not find him anywhere.

" And so I passed the places of all the King's ministers; I passed a sea of wine, where the King's Friend had spoken beautiful words; I passed a forest where every bird spoke, and I knew the Counsellor had been there; and I passed a stone upon which the Sage had graven the image of the Hand that held the past and future of the world; I walked upon a heap of pebbles that blazed like a fiery wheel, and I saw that the pebbles were jewels, and knew that the King's Treasurer had been in that place; and I came to a wilderness where a lone tree stood, and at the foot of the tree the earth was wounded as by the stab of a great sword, and from that opening there came a martial song of war; then I knew that you had passed that way, but I did not find you there."

The Hero answered, " I too passed over all those places, and in the desert I gathered seven hairs of the child, and they have all the colours of the rainbow. So I sat there, and took pleasure in looking upon the child's hairs. I remained there for a long time, and did not eat. But at last I was very hungry, and I arose, and went, but forgot my staff there."

"I saw your staff, and knew you had been in that place, too," said the Master.

"From there, I went on until I came to a number of people who made me their king. Then I went out to conquer the world, but it is not because I desire to rule the world, only that I hope to find the Princess, and our Child, and the King and Queen and all our company."

Then the Master remembered his mission and said, "What can we do with the people of this city? They are fallen into a terrible error, for they worship only riches."

At this, the Hero shook his head. "I once heard the King declare that men may be rid of any error, except the worship of gold," he said. "And the only way to rid them of the worship of gold is the way of the Sword."

Then the Master asked of the Hero, "Do not attack them at once, but give them yet a while, for they have sent me to you."

Because of his friendship for the Master, the Hero set aside a number of days' respite for the city; then the two friends arranged signs by which they would send messages to each other, and the Master went on his way.

As he went, he saw a number of people on the road; they were carrying many large tomes, and they were wrapped in prayer-shawls, and as they went they sang in praise of heaven. At this, the Master was startled, so he began to pray. He stood and prayed, and they stood and prayed; but at last the people said to him, "Who are you?" And he said to them, "Who are you?"

They answered, " When the whirlwind came over the world, and the people divided to seek kings for themselves, we were those who declared that holiness was the greatest of all things, and therefore we seek a master of prayer to be our king."

And when they heard him pray, their eyes were opened to all the mysteries, and they saw that he was a great man learned in the Torah, and they said, " Be our king! " So the Master became their king, and went with them.

Meanwhile the money-worshippers returned to their old ways and sacrificed beast-men to their men-gods; but no help came against the Warrior. The days passed, and the time he had given them was nearly gone. So they decided that they would do as they had planned to do at first, and send for help to that rich land where every man was a god. They chose seven of their own gods, and sent them on their way. But as the emissaries went on the road, they saw a man walking. The staff that he carried was encrusted with jewels so costly that it alone was worth more than any of their gods, and the man wore a cap covered with diamonds that were worth, to them, all the stars in heaven. The men-gods fell down to his feet, and desired to sacrifice themselves for him, but he would not permit them to do so. Instead, he took them up on a hill and showed them the treasures that were there, for he was the King's Treasurer. When the money-worshippers saw the treasures, they cried, " You are the god of gods! " And they decided that there was no need for them to go to the country where all men were gods, for surely the god of gods alone could help them. So they said to him, " Will you come to our city and be our king of kings? " He went with them, and when he came into the city he would not allow any sacrifices to be made to him. But when they told him of the Conqueror who threatened the city, he cried, " Perhaps it is the Hero whom I knew in olden times! " Then the Treasurer went out to the invading army, and asked to be taken to the Hero.

When the Treasurer and Hero met, they recognized each other, and rejoiced, and the Hero cried, " The Master of Prayer has been here too! " Then they told each other how they had sought each other, and the Treasurer said, " I, too, passed over the places where all our friends had been; only your place, and the place of the Master, I never found."

And at last they remembered to speak of the city of money-worshippers. " There is only one way to cure them," the Hero repeated, " and that is the way of the Sword."

" Give them a little more time," the Treasurer asked. So the Hero gave them more time, and the Treasurer returned to the city and spoke again to the people, trying to draw them out of their error.

And this time the money-worshippers listened, for when the Master had spoken against riches they had thought him mad, but now it was their own god of gods who spoke as the Master had spoken, and they thought, " Perhaps these strangers are not mad "; and they said to him, " If our way is wrong, show us a way out of it."

Then the Treasurer told them of the marvellous Sword and said, " You must go the way of the Sword, and there you will be healed."

Again the richest men of the city were chosen, to go with the Treasurer in search of the way of the Sword. They dressed themselves in their costliest garments, all overhung with gold and silver, and started upon their journey. But first the Treasurer went secretly to the Hero and said, " I am taking them on a journey, but I hope on the way to find the King, and all our companions."

" Let me go with you, then! " said the Hero. And he disguised himself so that the rich men might not be frightened at having the Warrior amongst them; and then he sent a message to the Master telling him of the journey. The Master came hastily, saying, " Let me, too, go with you; perhaps we will find the King and all the court." They took him with them, while all the people of the Master's land prayed for the success of the journey.

So they went, and they came to the borders of a kingdom; a watcher stood on the road. " What sort of kingdom is this? " they asked of him.

" This is the kingdom of the wise," he said. " For when the whirlwind upset the world, we were those who said that the greatest of all things is wisdom, and we sought a sage to rule over us. One knew the ways of the stars, and another could see into the waters, but at last we found a man who sat upon a stone, and studied his own hand.

" ' What wisdom have you? ' " we asked of him. And he answered, ' Only the wisdom that is within my own soul.' So we made him our king."

Then the Master, the Hero, the Treasurer, and their seven rich companions, were taken to the hall of Wisdom, and the king upon the throne was truly their friend the Sage. There was great joy amongst them, and then they spoke of all the others that had not been found, and then they spoke of their journey.

"We seek a way to rid these men of the folly of money-worship," the Treasurer said, "for I am the king of their kingdom."

"We are all fallen into folly," the Sage replied. "Some worship honour, some worship lust, and some worship death itself; and even we who worship wisdom have fallen into unbelief and empty questioning. But of all these follies men can be healed, except only the folly of gold."

Then he too went with them to find the way of the Sword, while they said, "Have you no longer that marvellous Hand upon which all the ways were shown?" The Sage answered, "I have the Hand, but I know that its secret is for the King alone to read, and since the King is lost I do not look upon the thing itself, but I have made an image of the Hand, which guides me."

They came to a land where men stood and spoke with each other. And men came eagerly towards them, saying, "We are the people who sought a Master of Words for our king. At first we crowned a madman who babbled in many languages, but then we heard a man who stood in the forest. He spoke, and the birds and the stones and the trees heard him, and answered. He sang, and they answered his song. So we said to him, 'Be our king,' and now he rules over us." Indeed, this was the King's Counsellor, and he went with the others.

They continued on their journey, and came to another kingdom, and found a soldier asleep; they wakened him and asked, "Who is your king?"

"We had a king whom we found drunk in the

road," he said; "but afterwards we came to a man who stood by a sea of wine. We asked him to be our king."

The Sage knew at once that the sea of wine must have been made by the King's Friend. So they came to him, and knew him, and he was filled with joy. "Let me go with you," he cried. "Perhaps we will find the others of the court."

Then they came to another land, where they found the watchman lying with a woman. "This is the land of beauty," he told them, "and our queen is a beautiful woman. For one day in the wilderness we came upon a woman so beautiful that the very trees bowed their fruit to her hand. But her beauty was sorrowful, and she sat very still with her head bowed, and sang a lullaby, while from her breasts there flowed a stream of purest milk. Then we begged her, 'Be our queen!' So she rules over us, but no man may approach her, for she awaits her true husband, and mourns the loss of her child."

They knew that the watchman spoke of the Princess, and they hastened to the court. The Hero took her in his arms, for he had found his wife, and they rejoiced together. The people of that kingdom desired him to be their king, and remain with them, but the Hero and the Princess said, "We must go and seek our Child."

They went with the others, and came to a kingdom where there were no watchmen. A man stood singing, and they asked of him, "Who is your king?"

"We are those who sought a king more pure than all other men," he told them. "And we said, 'We shall know his purity by the food upon which he lives.' At last we came upon a stream of milk, and by the stream there sat a Child, and he fed only upon the milk. We made him our king, and our king is a one-year-old babe! "

They ran at once to see the Child, and they knew him, and he knew them, for he was wondrous wise; then the mother and the father and the child rejoiced with one another, and the ministers rejoiced, and the rich men were happy, though they did not know for what.

But the King and the Queen had not yet been found, and all the company went forth on the quest, and they took the Child with them.

There was a land between two mountains, where watchmen stood in black armour, and would not let them pass.

" Who is your king? " the Warrior asked.

" We are of those who chose death as the end of all things, and for our king we took a man who had murdered his mother and father. But afterwards we found a woman who stood by a sea of blood, and moaned, and we said, ' Surely she has died more deaths than he.' So we killed our king, and we asked the woman to rule over us."

They went into the dungeon of death, and when the Queen saw them she cast aside her black veils, all but one heaviest, for " My husband has not been found," she said.

The Queen went with them, and they came to a land that was fair and green. A shepherd stood on a hill, and they asked of him, " Who is your king? "

" We are of those who chose honour as the greatest of all things, and at first an old gypsy ruled over us, but one day we came to this hill, and upon the hill there was seated an old man. His beard was white, and the wind went softly about his hair. There was a crown upon his head, and his aspect was of such wondrous peace and dignity that a wild faun came and knelt to him and kissed his hand."

"We said, 'Be our king!' and he rules over us."

Then they came to the top of the hill, and the King was truly their King, and so the holy court was come together again, and there was joy on earth and in heaven; and the rich men saw, and wondered.

Then each minister told the King of the errors of his people, and the King sent the Master to bring the peoples out of their strange errors; but there was no way to help those who worshipped money.

At last the Hero reminded the King, "I once heard the King say that there was only one way to bring men out of the error of riches, and that was the way of the Sword."

"That is true," said the King. "You must go the way of the Sword, and there you will find a path that turns and leads to a flaming mountain. But the flaming mountain is invisible, and on its top there lives a lion who comes down and falls upon the flocks, and kills and eats the sheep and the goats. From there you must go onward on another path, and you will come to the place where the daintiest of foods are prepared. It is far from the mountain, and yet it is fed by the fire of the mountain, for there is no fire in the hearth; and the hearth, too, is invisible, but you will know it by the two great birds who stand and fan the fire with the beating of their wings, making it rise or shrink according to the need. There, the daintiest of foods

are prepared, and only in those foods is the power to
make men forget the folly of gold. So you must lead
them against the wind, that they may scent the wonderful odour of these foods, and when they taste of
the food, they will forget riches."

The Hero led the band of rich men, and at last
they scented the odour of the food. " Let us eat some
of that food! " they cried. Then he turned them and
led them with the wind, and they began to smell a
terrible odour instead, and asked, " What is that
horrible stench?" He turned them again and led
them against the wind, so they caught the beautiful
delicate odour of the foods, and they cried, " Let us
only taste that delicious food! " But he turned them
once more, and the putrid stench came to their nostrils, and they ran, but the stench grew. " Where can
it come from? " they asked.

" You see that there is nothing near you that can
have so bad an odour," the Hero said, " and since you
are running, and the odour remains with you, it must
be something upon yourselves that smells so ill! "

He turned them against the wind, and this time he
led them into the cave of wonderful delicacies, and
gave them to eat of the foods.

As soon as they had tasted the delicacies, the rich
men knew that it was their own gold and silver that
had smelled so ill, and they began to throw their gold
and silver garments from them. They swiftly hurled
away all the money and jewels they had in their
pockets, and tore diamonds from their clothes, and
rings from their fingers; and the more they ate of the
wonderful food, the more ashamed they became of
riches, and whoever had a gulden or a penny left

threw it from him; some even buried their faces in the earth, while others tried to bury themselves alive to be free of the filth of money, and a few tore at their own skins to remove the odour of gold from themselves; for the food that they ate possessed so great a power of truth that the more money a man had, the greater was his shame.

The Hero saw, and prevented them from tearing themselves to pieces and from burying themselves alive; and when they had thoroughly cleansed themselves of their riches he said to them, " Come, let us go home! Now you have no more need to fear the Conqueror, so know that I myself am that dreaded warrior! "

Then they took with them enough of the wonderful delicacies for all their people, and they returned home to their kingdom, and gave morsels of the food to all the people to eat. At once the rich men who were called gods and kings and princes threw their gold from them, and buried their heads in the ground in shame, and the little men who were called beasts and birds were also ashamed, and threw away their pennies.

When they had all been cleansed of their error, the Master came, and brought them forgiveness. Then the King and his Court were assembled once more, and the King ruled over the earth, and the secret ways were opened again, and each of the ministers returned to his place to renew his strength at its source; and all the peoples of the earth gave over their foolishness and lived in righteousness and peace, singing to Heaven.

THE SEVEN BEGGARS

THERE was once a king who had an only son, and while he lived the king decided to give his crown to the prince. He made a great festival to which all the noblemen of the kingdom came, and in the midst of pomp and ceremony the king placed the crown upon the head of his young son, saying, " I am one who can read the future in the stars, and I see that there will come a time when you will lose your kingdom, but when that time comes you must not be sorrowful; if you can be joyous even when your kingdom is lost, I too will be filled with joy. For you cannot be a true king unless you are a happy man."

The son became king, appointed governors, and ruled. He was a lover of learning, and in order to fill his court with wise men he let it be known that he would give every man whatever he desired, either gold or glory, in return for his wisdom; than all the people in that kingdom began to seek for knowledge, in order to get gold or glory from the king. And thus it was that the simplest fool in the land was wiser than the greatest sage of any other country; and in their search for learning, the people forgot the study of war, so the country was left open to the enemy.

Among the philosophers in the young king's court there were clever men and infidels who soon filled his mind with doubt. He would ask himself, " Who am I; why am I in the world? " Then he would heave a deep sigh, and fall into melancholy. Only when he would forget this doubt would he again become a happy king; but more often every day he thought, " Why am I in this world? " and sighed.

One day the invader came and attacked the unprotected kingdom, and all the people fled. Men and women left their fields and their homes, and the highways were filled with carts and wagons, with people on foot carrying infants in their arms. The fleeing people went through a forest, and there it befell that two five-year-old children were lost: a boy and a girl. After all the people had passed, the children heard each other crying. Then they went up to each other and joined hands, and wandered through the forest. Soon they were hungry, but they did not know where they could get food.

Just then they saw a beggar going through the woods, carrying his beggar's sack. They ran to him and clung to him.

" Where do you come from? " he asked.

" We do not know," the children answered.

He gave them bread to eat, and turned to go on his way. They begged him not to leave them alone, but he said, " I cannot take you with me." Then the children saw that he was blind, and they wondered how he found his way through the forest. But as he was leaving, he blessed them, saying, " May you be as I am, and as old as I am." Then he left them.

Night came, and the children slept. In the morning they cried again for food; then they saw another beggar. They began to talk to him, but he placed his fingers against his ears and showed them that he was deaf. He gave them bread to eat, enough for the day, and as he went he blessed them, saying, " May you be as I am."

THE SEVEN BEGGARS

On the third day when they cried for bread another beggar came, who stammered so that he could not speak to them. He, too, fed the children, but would not take them with him, and as he went away he blessed them with the wish that they might become like himself. And so each day as they wandered through the forest the children were fed: on the fourth day by a beggar with a crippled throat, then by a hunchback, then by a beggar who had no hands, and at last there came a beggar who had no feet. And each beggar left them with the wish that they might become as he was.

On the eighth day they came out of the forest to a town; they went to a house and asked for food, and as the people saw that they were only little children, they were given food and drink. So the children said to each other, " We will go on like this from one place to another, and we will always remain together." They made great beggar's sacks for themselves, for carrying whatever was given them, and they went over the countryside, into the towns, to the fairs, and into the cities. Wherever they went, they sat among the beggars, until they became known to all the poor folk on the roads as the " two children who were lost in the woods."

Years passed, the children grew. Once, when all the beggars of the kingdom were assembled at a fair in a great city, a leader among them thought, " Let us marry the children, one to another." He told his companions of this thought, and they told others, and when the children were told they said, " Good! " So it was decided to marry them at once. All that was needed was a place for the wedding. Then the mendicants remembered that the king was holding a festival, where food and drink would be provided to all who came. " That will be the wedding feast! " they cried.

The beggars went to the king's garden and received meat and bread and wine; then they dug a great cave in the ground, large enough to hold a hundred people; they covered the cave with branches and with earth, and they set up a wedding canopy within the cave. There they made the wedding, and feasted, with eating and dancing and merriment. But the children sat together, and all at once they remembered their days in the forest, and the blind beggar who had been the first to bring them food. And they longed for the blind beggar to be at their wedding.

Just then they heard him call out, " Here I am! I have come to your marriage! And as a wedding gift I bestow upon you the blessing I wished you before: may you live to be as I am, and as old as I am. You must not believe that I am blind; I am not blind at all, but in my sight the entire world is not worth the blink of an eye, and so, as I never look upon the world, I have the appearance of one who is blind. I am very old," he said, " but I am quite young, and I have not yet begun to live. Nevertheless I am aged, and it is not I alone who say this, but I have the word of the great Eagle. I will tell you the story.

" Once there was a ship sailing on a sea; a great storm came, and the ship was broken, but the people were saved. They climbed to a high tower, and in the tower they found clothing and food and wine and everything that was good. In order to pass the time pleasantly, they said, ' Let each of us tell the story of his oldest memory, and we shall see whose memory is longest.' Aged and young were there, and the first that spoke was the eldest of them all, and he was white with years.

" ' What shall I tell you? ' he said. ' I even remember when the apple was cut from the bough.' Though many sages were among them, none understood the meaning of his tale, yet they all agreed that the story was indeed of olden times.

" Then the second eldest in years said, as one who wonders and admires, ' That is truly an ancient tale! I remember that happening, and I even remember the candle that burned.'

" Everyone agreed that this was even an older story than the first, and they wondered how a younger man could remember a story of older times; then they asked the third eldest to tell a story in his turn.

" ' I even remember when the fruit first began to grow,' he said, ' for then the fruit was only beginning to take form.'

" ' That is yet a more ancient story,' all agreed. But the fourth in years spoke: ' I remember when the seed was brought that was to be planted in the fruit '; and the fifth said, ' I remember the sage who thought of the seed '; then the sixth, who was younger still, declared, ' I remember the taste of the fruit before the taste went into the fruit '; and the seventh said, ' I remember the odour of the fruit before the fruit had an odour '; but the eighth said, ' I remember the appearance of the fruit before the fruit could be seen, and I was but a child.' "

Then the blind beggar who was telling the story said, " I was the youngest in years among them in the tower, and when they had all spoken, I spoke. ' I remember all those things, and I remember the thing that is Nothing.'

" All who were there agreed that mine was a story of something far, far back, further than all the other happenings, and they wondered at the child whose memory was longer than that of the eldest man. But there came a beating of wings and a knocking upon the walls of the tower, and we saw a great Eagle come.

" He cried, ' You have been poor men long enough, you may return now to your treasures.' And he added, ' I will take you out of the tower, the eldest first, and so according to your ages.' Then he took me out first, and the eldest in years he took out last, and when we were all taken out of the tower the Eagle said to us, ' I can explain all the tales that have been told; for he who remembered when the apple was cut from the bough remembered how at his birth he was cut from his mother; the candle that burned was the babe in the womb, for it is written in *gemara* that while the child is in the womb a candle burns over his head; and he that remembers when the fruit began to grow remembers how his limbs first began to form in his mother's womb; he that recalls the bringing of the seed remembers how he was conceived; and he that knows the wisdom that created the seed remembers when conception was but in the mind; the taste that preceded the fruit is the memory of Being; the scent is Spirit; and vision is the Soul; but the child that remembers Nothing is greater than them all, for he remembers that which existed before Being, Spirit, or Soul; he remembers the life that hovered upon the threshold of eternity.' Then the Eagle said, ' Return to your vessels, for they are your bodies that were broken, and they are built again.' He blessed them all, but to me he said, ' You must come with me, for you are as I am, you are very old, but still young, and you have not yet begun to live.' And so you see that it was from the great Eagle himself that I learned the secret of my age and of my youth: and today I give you this as my gift: that you may be as I am, and as old as I am."

When the blind beggar had spoken there was great joy and merriment among the wedding guests, and the bride and groom were happy.

On the second day of the seven days of celebration, the bride and groom remembered the second beggar who had fed them in the forest, and they were lonely for the deaf one; but as they thought of him, he called, " Here I am! " And he came and kissed them, and said, " Today I bequeath upon you as a wedding gift that which I once gave you in blessing: be as I am, and live a life as good as mine; surely you believe that I am deaf; I am not deaf at all, but the error of the world is not worth my hearing, for the world is all error, and the cries of its people are but folly, and even their joy is filled with error; what need have I to hear evil when I lead a life so good and flawless, for see, I have made even the people of the Land of Luxury understand that there is nothing in the world so good to eat as bread, and no drink better than water.

" Once all the people of the Land of Luxury came together and vied with each other in telling of the ease in which they lived; one man spoke of the humming-bird's wings upon which he feasted, and another told of the rare wine he drank, and each boasted of a luxury greater than his neighbour's, until I said, 'I live a life of rarer ease and luxury than yours!' They all looked at my beggar's mantle, and laughed, but I said to them, 'I know a land where a garden grows that is filled with trees overladen with marvellous fruits. Once the fruits had every tempting odour and flavor and beauty in the world, and every good thing that grows was in that garden. A gardener watched over the trees, and pruned them, and cared for their growth; but the gardener has disappeared and cannot be found, there is no one to take care of the trees, and the people live only from the wild growth of the dropped seed. Even of this, they might have lived well; but a tyrant king invaded their land. He did not harm the people, and he did not himself spoil their garden, but he left behind him three companies of soldiers: one company made the taste of the garden into bitterness, the other made the odour into stench, and the third made its beauty into clouded darkness.'

" Then I said to the people of the Land of Luxury, 'Help the people of this other kingdom, for the taste, the beauty, and the odour is gone from their fruit, and if you do not help them, the same evil may reach to your land!' So they set out for the spoiled kingdom, but lived in luxury on their journey, until they came close to the garden, and then the beauty, and the taste, and the delectable odour began to go from their own food, and they did not know what to do. So I gave them some of my bread to eat, and my water to drink, and they tasted all the riches of their fine foods, and they breathed all the delectable odours, and they saw all the beauties of the fruits in the bread and water that I gave them. Meanwhile the people of the spoiled kingdom remembered that their gardener was of one root with the people of the Land of Luxury, so they decided to send envoys to that kingdom of plenty. The envoys met on the road with the people from the Land of Luxury, and they took council together, and sent me first into the spoiled land.

" Then I went into the city and saw people assembled in the street; I listened to them, and heard one whisper to the other, while the other laughed and whispered to a third, and I knew it was filth that they uttered. I went further, and saw people quarrel and go to a court and quarrel again and go to another court, until the whole city was filled with judges and bribery; and the city was also filled with lust. Then I knew that the invading king had left his three battalions in the city to spread the three diseases: of filth that had spoiled the taste in their mouth, and bribery that had made their eyes blind, and lust that was a stench in their nostrils. So I said to them, ' Let us drive out these strangers; and perhaps the gardener will be found again.' Then the men from the Land of Luxury, who ate of my bread and water, and were well of sight and scent and hearing, helped me, and wherever they caught one of the soldiers, they drove him from the land.

" There was a madman that wandered in the streets and cried continually that he was a gardener; everyone laughed at him, and some even threw stones at him. Then I said to them, ' Perhaps he is really the gardener; bring him to me.' They brought him, and I saw that he was indeed the gardener, and he was restored to the garden. So the people again knew the taste of their fruit, and the scent, and the beauty of it; and in reward I was given the good life, and today I bestow it upon you." Again the wedding guests rejoiced, and the bride and groom were happy.

On the third day the children cried, " What has become of the stammerer! " Then the heavy-tongued beggar came, and embraced them, and said, " Here I am! " In a clear voice he spoke to them. " On that day when we met in the woods I blessed you with the wish that you might be as I am; and today I bestow it upon you as a gift: for look you, you believe that I am dumb, yet in truth I am not heavy-tongued, but I have no use for all men's words except those that are uttered in praise of God, and all other earthly words are not worthy of utterance. Indeed I am gifted with speech, and can sing so beautifully that there is not one creature in the world, bird or beast, that will not stop to hear my song. And I have proof of this from that great man who is called the Truly Godly Man. For once all the sages of the world came together to prove who was cleverest; the first said, ' I have brought iron out of the earth '; and the second said, ' I have found a way to make brass '; and a third knew how to make tin, and another could make silver, and still another had discovered gold; then one came who had made guns and cannon for war, and yet another had discovered how to make gun-powder. But one said, ' I am wiser than all of you, for I am as wise as the day.' They did not understand him, and so he said, ' If all of your wisdom were taken together it would not make a single hour, for one of you takes things out of the earth and mixes them together to make powder, and another takes iron out of the earth, and another brass, but all of your silver, and iron, and brass, and gold is taken out of the earth that God made in a day, and all of the things that you take out, if put together, would not make a single hour of that day; while I, I am as wise as the entire day! '

" Then I asked him, ' What day? ' And he turned to me and said, ' No matter which day it may be, you are wiser than I, for you have asked, " What day? " ' "

" And I explained my wisdom to them, saying, " You must know that time does not exist of itself, and that days are made only of good deeds. It is through men who perform good deeds that days are born, and so time is born; and I am he who goes all about the world to find those men who secretly do good deeds: I bring their deeds to the great man who is known as the Truly Godly Man, and he turns them into time; then time is born, and there are days and years.

" And this is the life of the world: At the far end of the world there is a mountain, on the mountain-top is a rock, and a fountain of water gushes from the rock. This you know: that everything in the world possesses a heart, and the world itself has a great heart. The heart of the world is complete, for it has a face, and hands, and breasts, and toes, and the littlest toe of the world's heart is more worthy than any human heart. So at one end of the earth there is the fountain that flows from the rock on the mountain-top, and at the other end is the earth's heart. And the heart desires the mountain spring; it remains in its place far at the other end of the earth, but it is filled with an unutterable longing, it burns with an endless desire for the distant fountain of water. In the day, the sun is like a blazing whip upon the heart, because of its longing for the spring; but when the heart is utterly weak from the punishment of the sun, a great bird comes and spreads its wings and gives the heart rest. But even while it rests, it longs for the mountain spring, and it looks toward the peak of the mountain, for if it were to lose sight of the spring for but one instant, the heart would cease to live.

" Because of its great longing, it sometimes tries to go to the fountain, but if it goes nearer to the foot of the mountain it can no longer see the spring on the top of the mountain, and so it must remain far away, for only from a distance may a mountain peak be seen. And if it were for an instant to lose sight of the spring, the heart would die, and then all the world would die, for the life of the world and everything in it is in the life of its heart.

" So the heart remains longing at the other end of the earth, longing for the spring that cannot come toward it, for the spring has no share in Time, but lives on a mountain peak far above the time that is on earth. And the mountain spring could not be of the earth at all, since it has no share in the earth's time, but for the earth's heart, which gives the spring its day. And as the day draws to its close, and time is ended, the heart becomes dark with grief, for when the day is done the mountain spring will be gone from the earth, and then the earth's heart will die of longing, and when the heart is dead all the earth and all the creatures upon the earth will die.

" And so, as the day draws to a close, the heart begins to sing farewell to the fountain; it sings its grief in wildly beautiful melody, and the mountain spring sings farewell to the heart, and their songs are filled with love and eternal longing.

But the Truly Godly Man keeps watch over them, and in that last moment before the day is done, and the spring is gone, and the heart is dead, and the world is ended, the good man comes and gives a new day to the heart; then the heart gives the day to the spring, and so they live again. As the day comes, it is brought with melody, and with strangely beautiful words that contain all wisdom; for there are differences between the days, there are Sabbaths and Mondays, and there are holidays, and days of the first of the month; and each day comes with its own song.

" All these days that the Godly man gives to the heart of the world he has through me, for it is I who go about the world to find the men who do good deeds, and it is from their deeds that time is born, for each deed becomes a melody in my mouth, and from the melody the Godly man makes a day, and the day is given to the heart, and she sings it to the fountain. Therefore I am wiser than the sage who said he had the wisdom of an entire day, for from the Truly Godly Man I have a gift enabling me to sing the songs and know the wisdom of all the days on earth. And today I bestow upon you, as a wedding gift, the power to be as I am." At once there was joy among them, and the beggars all sang together.

So they ended that day with joy. But on the fourth day the children longed for the beggar with the twisted throat, and he came and said, " I am here! Once before I blessed you that you might be as I am, and today I bestow upon you this wedding gift: be as

I am! You believe that I have a twisted throat, but see, my throat is really beautiful and straight, but there are foolish and evil things in this world, and I would not have any of them come into me through my throat, therefore my throat seems twisted. It is really clear and beautiful, and I have a voice that is wonderful in song, for through my throat I can imitate the call and the song of every creature that lives! I have this power from the land of melody, for there is a land where everyone, from the king to the smallest child, is wondrously skilled in music; some play the harp, others the violin, and some play many instruments.

"Once, all of their greatest musicians came together, and each began to boast of his skill: one could play upon a harp, another upon a violin, and still another could play upon a harp and a violin, while there was one who said he could play upon every musical instrument; then a man declared that he could imitate the sound of a harp with his voice, and another could imitate the sound of violins, one could imitate a drum, and still another could make a noise like a cannon. I too was there, and I said, ' My voice is more wonderful than all your voices. For if you are such great musicians, can you bring help to the suffering nations?' And I told them, ' There are two peoples whose countries lie a thousand miles apart, and when night comes over those lands the people cannot sleep. For with night, there comes a strange moaning and wailing, so drear, so heart-weary, that the very stones groan and weep. And when the people hear this sound, they too must begin to moan and weep; every night all the men and women, and even the children of these countries lie awake moaning and weeping with the sorrow that is over them. And you, who are so skilled in music, can you help those people? '

" Then they asked me, ' Will you lead us there? ' And I said, ' Yes! ' So they all arose and I led them. We came to one of the countries, and at night we heard the strange moaning; then even the sages from the land of melody wept and moaned, but they could do nothing.

" ' Can you tell me,' I said to them, ' where this sound comes from? ' "

" ' And do you know? ' they asked.

" ' I know. For there were two beautiful birds that had mated together, and they were the only two of their kind. But once they were lost, one from the other, and they flew everywhere, each seeking its mate, until they became weary, and their hope was gone from them, for they knew they were far from each other. Each settled alone where it was; one built his nest in his land, and the other built her nest where she was a thousand miles away; now when night comes the two birds begin to lament, each for the other, and it is their moaning lament that the people hear, and they too must keen with the birds, until there is no rest for them at night.'

" The sages would not believe me, but said, ' Can you take us to the bird's place? ' I said, ' I can take you there, but you will not be able to bear the weight of it by night or by day, for at night the lament is so great that you may not come near it, and during the day flocks of birds come to her and to him, to cheer them in their loneliness, and all the birds sing merrily until the joy is so great as to be unbearable: this joy cannot be heard from afar, but if you come near it, you will succumb.' Then the sages asked, 'Can you right this thing?' And I told them that I could make my voice like the voice of any living being, and that I also could send my voice to all places on earth, so that it might not be heard where I stood, but would be heard far away.

"I said to the wise men, 'Will you go with me to a place that is neither in one land or the other, but lies between them? For from that place I will send my voice with the sound of her voice to him, and I will send my voice with the sound of his voice to her, so that each will hear the other's voice, they will listen, and tremble, and rise and spread their wings and fly toward the place of the voice, and so they will meet together where I stand.'

"Then I led them to a place that lay between the two countries; the place was in a forest, and the ground was covered with snow. I stood and sang, but the men could hear no sound come from me. Only, they heard the sound of a door opening and closing, and they heard the sound of a gun, and they heard the barking of a hound as it ran over the snow for the kill. Yet they saw nothing. But I had sent my voices, and soon there were two pair of wings above us. Then the men from the land of melody understood how I had brought the two birds together, and they agreed that mine was the most wonderful voice of all, for I could send it wherever I chose; and so today I bestow upon you this gift: that you may be as I am." He finished speaking, and all the beggars made merry, and sang.

On the fifth day the children, in the midst of merriment, sighed, " If the hunchback were only here! " And there he stood, and said, " I have come to your wedding, my children! And do you remember how I blessed you that you might be as I am? Today I bestow my wish upon you as a wedding gift: be as I am! It seems to you that I am a hunchback, but indeed my shoulders are wide and straight and strong, and I have proof of this from the land where people once came together to see who could bear the heaviest burden upon the slightest support; then one said, ' The top of my head is a small enough place and yet I carry myriads of creatures, with all their needs upon it! ' But they made sport of him, while another man said, ' You are like a creature I once saw: I thought he sat by a mountain, but when I came near I knew that it was a mountain of refuse that he had thrown out of himself! ' Then a third man said, ' I know of a small place that bears a burden greater than itself, for I have an orchard where fruit trees grow, and the fruit on the trees could many times cover the earth out of which the trees grow.'

" Many people said, ' That is indeed a great thing come out of a little thing,' but another man declared, ' I have a tiny garden so beautiful that princes and kings come to walk in it; then my garden is only a small place, but it has borne up the weight of a kingdom! '

" Still another spoke, saying: ' My speech is a slender support that bears great burdens, for I am a minister to a king; I hear the complaints and the praises, the petitions and supplications of all his subjects; all these utterances are taken within me, and my word bears them to the king! '

" But a fifth man answered him: ' My silence is less and yet greater than your word, for there are torrents of accusation against me, and curses, and foul names, but my only reply is silence, and my silence bears up against all the cries of my enemies; my silence is a little thing, and yet it withstands a great storm.'

" Then another contender spoke; he was hidden, because he was small, but he said: ' I am a little man, and yet I bear up a great burden; for I know a needy one who is far taller than myself, and though he is a Greater Light he cannot find his way! I lead him, and were it not for me he might fall, and lose his path.'

" I, too, was there, and I said, ' It is true that some among you have the power of bearing up great burdens, for I have understood all that you have said, even to the last of you, who spoke of leading a Greater Light: for the little man is greater than the greatest of you, since it is the wheel of the moon that he speaks of, for the moon is called a Greater Light and a Blind Light since her light is not her own, and though he is a little man he leads the great wheel of the moon through the heavens, and his deed is a help to all the world, for the world has need of the moon. Nevertheless, in me there is a support that is smaller and bears weightier burdens than any of these; for you know that every beast in the world has his favourite tree whose shadow is pleasant to him, and there he makes his place; and every bird has his favourite bough, and there he sits; but once it was asked, is there not a tree in the world in whose shade all beasts might linger, and upon whose boughs all birds might rest? It was answered, there is such a tree! and it is indeed a

pleasant tree, for all the beasts of the earth are assembled in its shade, they lie happily together, yet
there is no preying of one upon the other; and all
the birds sing in the boughs of the tree. Then my
people cried, ' How can we find that tree? ' And one
wanted to go to the east, and another to the south,
so that they became all confused. But a wise man said,
' Why do you quarrel over the way? First, know
whether you can come to the tree at all, for the tree
has three roots: the first is Belief, the second is Fear
of God, and the third is Poverty; and the trunk of the
tree is Truth. Only those who possess these things
can approach the tree.'

"The people asked among themselves, but not
many of them possessed the three qualities that are
Belief, and Fear, and Poverty; those few might go,
but they would not go and leave the others behind.
' We are one people,' they said, ' and all of us must
go, or none.' So they waited, and laboured amongst
themselves, that all the people might possess the
three needed qualities. And when all had Belief, and
Fear, and Poverty, they found that they were agreed
on the one way to go to the tree; they went for a long
time, and then they saw the tree, and they saw that it
did not stand on any place at all! And since it did not
stand anywhere, how might they come to it? But I,"
the hunchback said, "was there among them, and I
said, ' I can take you to that place. For the tree is not
of this earth, but of a place higher than this earth.
See, upon my back I have a little place where great
burdens may be borne: it is a tiny thing that is on the
very edge of this world, where a higher world begins,
and so, upon my little hump, one may go from this

world to the world that is higher than here.' Then I
carried them all upon my hump, from the earth to
the tree that stood above the earth, and so you see
that I carried a great burden upon a small support.
For when I brought them to the tree they said, ' You
are indeed the master of us all, for upon the smallest
place you have borne the greatest burden.' And thus
I have their word for my deeds, for upon my back
I carry all the ills and the woes and the sins of the
people of the world. And now I bestow my gift upon
you, that you may be as I am."

Then they were merry, but on the sixth day they
remembered the beggar whose hands were withered,
and they longed for him. Then he came and said,
" Here I am! " and he embraced the children, and
gave them his gift. " In the forest I blessed you, that
you might be as I am, and today I bestow that upon
you as a wedding gift: be as I am. You believe that I
cannot use my hands," he said, " but indeed my
hands are strong, only there is nothing in the world
worth their use, and I save their strength for other
deeds. See, I have proof of their strength from the
Palace of Water.

" There was a princess who was ill, and many people came together, each boasting that he had the
power to heal her in his hands. One said, ' I have such
a power in my hands that when I shoot an arrow I
can seize it and bring it back! ' Then I said to him,
' What sort of arrows can you bring back? For there
are ten kinds of arrows, since there are ten sorts of
poison that may be put upon arrows, and one is
stronger than the other! ' And again I asked him,
' Can you draw back the arrow only while it is still in

its flight, or can you draw it back even after it has stricken its victim?'

"He answered, 'I can draw it back even after it has stricken its victim; but it is only the first kind of arrow that I can draw back.'

"'If you can only draw back the first kind of arrow,' I said to him, 'you cannot heal the princess!'

"Another man was there who said he had such a power in his hands that whenever he took something from someone, instead of taking, he gave. Then I knew he was a master of Good, and I said, 'What sort of Good do you give?'

"'The tenth sort,' he told me. So I said, 'You cannot heal the princess, for you could never come to her chamber; she is surrounded by ten walls, and you can only pass through the first of them.'

"A man was there who said he had such a power in his hands that he gave wisdom to whomever he touched, and it was he who had given wisdom to all the sages of the world; but I said to him, 'There are ten degrees of wisdom, and which sort of wisdom can you give?' He could give only one of the ten, then I said, 'You cannot heal the princess, for you could never find out her pain; there are ten degrees of pain, and you know only one, for you can give only one sort of wisdom with your hands.'

"Another was there, who said, 'I have so great a power in my hands that I can catch a stormy wind as it flies, and hold it, and let it out as a gentle wind or strong, however I desire.' But I said to him, 'There are ten winds, and which wind can you catch?'

"'The whirlwind!' he answered. Then I told him, 'You cannot heal the princess, for you know the melody of only a single wind, and there are ten winds, and each wind has a melody, and the princess may be healed only through song.'

" Then they cried to me, ' What sort of power have you in your hands? ' And I told them, ' All the nine parts of each of the things you cannot do, I can do.'

" And this is the story: There was a king who fell in love with a princess, and he called sorcerers and made magic spells over her until he caught her in his love and brought her to his palace. But once at night he dreamed that the princess arose from her bed and murdered him. The king was terribly frightened; he called all his sages to him and asked them the meaning of his dream. They told him, ' The dream is true. As you dreamed, so it will happen.' At this, he did not know what to do. He could not kill the princess, for he loved her; and he could not send her away, for he had suffered so much for her, and if he sent her away someone else would have her, and if she went to someone else she might return to do what she had done in his dream; yet he was afraid to keep her by him. The king did not know what to do, so he did nothing; and as the days passed his love for the princess waned, for he thought of her always as the murderess in his dream; and as his love waned the spell fell from the princess, and her love waned, until it became hatred, and she hated the king. Then she ran from the palace; but he sent out searchers to find her. The searchers returned and said, ' We have seen her wandering near the Palace of Water! '

" For the king had a palace that was the most wonderful of all places on earth: it was built entirely of water! The walls of the palace were of clear water, they stood and glimmered in the sun; the earth upon which the palace stood was deep water, and the gardens about the palace were of water, and they were filled with all manner of fruits and flowers, luscious and gold and green, all liquid as the sea. The palace and its garden were surrounded by ten watery walls; no man might come into that place, for surely he would be drowned.

"When the guards told the king that they had seen the princess wandering near the walls of water, he cried, 'We will catch her there!' and the king went out with his men to pursue the princess. But as she saw them coming, she was seized with terror, she thought she would rather die than be taken by them again; she looked at the walls and thought, 'perhaps I can even pass through the walls and reach the palace!' Then she ran into the water.

"As the king saw her run into the water, he cried, 'My dream was true! She is a sorceress!' And he shouted to his men, 'Kill her!' They shot their arrows after her, and each of the ten arrows struck the princess, and upon each arrow was another of the ten poisons. But she found the gates beneath the watery walls, and she passed through the ten walls, and fell within the palace, and there she lies in a swoon.

"Only I can heal her, for only he who has the ten virtues in his hands can pass through the ten walls of water. And when the king and his men sought to run after her, they all were drowned in the sea.

"But under the walls of water are the ten winds, and each wind blows beneath the sea and raises the waters up into a wall, and while the wind remains under the ocean the water remains on high; but I can seize the ten winds, and I can pass through the ten walls of water, and I can go into the palace and draw the ten poisoned arrows from the princess; and I can heal her ten wounds with my ten fingers, for through ten melodies she may be healed entirely.

" And then they understood that I might truly heal the princess, they agreed that the greatest power was in my hands, and now I bestow that power upon you, my children! "

There was joy greater than ever before, all that day until the next day, and then they longed for the coming of the legless beggar. But now the story is heavy to tell, for every word in it is burdened with meaning; and whoever is filled with the knowledge of the book of mysteries may understand, for the meaning of the arrows that could be drawn back is written in its passages, and the meaning of the virtue that could stand against the walls of water is in the lines: ' And their righteousness is as the waves of the sea! ' and the ten sorts of wounds, and the ten healing melodies are also written in the Zohar.

But of the last beggar, who did not have the use of his feet, what may be told? For in his story is the end of the beginning, and of the tale of the young prince who asked, " Who am I, and why am I in the world? " and who sighed when he was told to be joyous.

For with the coming of the seventh beggar, there will come the answer, but that may not be revealed, and cannot be revealed, and will not be known until Messiah comes. May he come soon, and in our day.